To Dominic

Fighting Captain Chemo

Peter Vickers

Thanks for getting in the ring with me

12/11/09

ISBN No: 978-1-905546-57-2

Printed & published by Pen2print
Units 9/10 Ferrybridge Workspace
Pontefract Road, Ferrybridge
West Yorkshire, WF11 8PL
www.pen2print.co.uk

To Stella, for helping me through
the two biggest crises of my life

Fighting Captain Chemo

In the 1981/82 season I used to go and watch Darlington Football Club play at the Feethams Ground in Division Four as it was called then. Two good players they had, David Speedie and Alan Walsh. As you went through the turnstile you paid and then handed in any Persil vouchers you had saved up. The football club could exchange them for the team's rail tickets to away games. As a fan, you could also sponsor Alan Walsh's right sock or David's shorts but you somehow knew it was the anonymous left back who was wearing yours. In the ground there were just over six hundred resilient fans, including me.

Last summer about one hundred people came through a different kind of turnstile and played an active part in my illness and circumstances . Each person brought a voucher in the form of a gift, sponsorship, friendship, hope, humour, love, medical support or practical help. I have met another group of people too - those who haven't had the strength to push their way through a turnstile, people more ill than me but who have in their own way been supportive. I get the feeling that over the coming months and years there will be enough people helping and visiting me to have formed a fair sized crowd at Feethams.

Who shall I dedicate this is to? So many people have already given me so much motivation to get better but the answer is clear enough and predictable by now, my lovely Kate. She hates all things medical and faints at a blood test, yet moves from strength to strength each day. A loyal supporter. What a lucky bloke I am.

Introduction

I lose things. It can be amusing, nothing serious but tedious to live with I should imagine. My briefcase often gets run over by my reversing car on the way to work. I can lose keys between the car park and the front door. I see my car, try to unlock it but set off an alarm - it's not my car, just the same colour. Last spring, I rode to work on my motorbike, (a Honda CB500) parked up, got off and locked up the adjacent bike to mine. By 5.00pm, the owner of the other bike was waiting and enraged.

It's not just vehicles. I haven't told Kate this yet but I once visited a greengrocer down our street when my youngest was only one year old. Halfway back up the hill I was wondering what I had forgotten and where my list had gone. The lady from the shop chased me and shouted 'You forgotten something?'
It was the lemons, I thought, how does she know?
'Your Joe, he's sat in his pushchair. We've given him a banana!'

Even animals have had to suffer the misfortunes of my forgetfulness. I remember getting to work after dropping the kids at school only to find a phone call from the head teacher awaiting me. I presumed it was something to do with one of the children. She was concerned about the dog I had left tied to a drainpipe. It had disturbed assembly with its barking and it was starting to rain..

Kids, vehicles, finance and animals. The list could go on. Airports, lost tickets or large cheques, fivers, tenners, let's not go much further. Suffice to say I have improved greatly since leaving my keys in the car, complete with identity, cheque book, a Swiss army knife, bankcards, a Mars Bar and my Graceland's tape. Kate nearly left me then, she liked that album. They all vanished along with the car. My lovely Peugeot 405 it seems provided the perfect drugs' den for three teenagers for nearly a

week! That was enough to pull me around. I am doing better.
You may have gathered by now that I don't cope too well in the wider world. Always something on my mind, sometimes serious, often just a flippancy. It's a big place, anything can happen and often does.

However, I have found a much smaller space, just the square footage you would find behind a hospital curtain - about 30 square feet, I'm not sure of the metric equivalent. It's my tiny empire. So far I have lost nothing, I know where things are, keep it tidy and receive all sorts of news, especially when the consultant visits. I leave my empire sometimes, not for long usually, get clean, come back, then visit someone else on the ward. Visitors come to me, the turnstile keeps humming and thank goodness for that.

In my wider world, despite some of the troubles I make for myself, I remain very fortunate. I work in Leeds and have a smashing job. I'm part of a great team which provides further education for adults with severe disabilities. In a strange way I have come to appreciate the team more since I have been ill as their support and thoughtfulness has been really helpful. The work itself takes me all over Leeds and often further away. I now lose things in Bradford, London and Nottingham too.

I am married to Kate and have four children. Sam and Rosie are now both at University and my two younger boys, Michael and Joe are in primary school. This is my second marriage. In 1993 my first wife left me for another bloke when Sam and Rosie were just infants. From the time she met him to the time she left took just three weeks. It is an understatement to say that we were devastated. He was, I believe, less forgetful than me but also much older and fatter. He still is. Being a single parent was a huge learning experience for me but that's another story which may surface later on.

Just as with so many other people, my job has formed a major part of my life and I am very lucky to earn a living doing something that I like. I work with inspiring students, teachers and support staff - but everything has changed since my holiday from work in the summer of 2008. My life has been turned upside down for a second time.

This story is written during my illness and I'm hoping that it will help me survive the difficulties, treatments and events. I remember how much writing helped me in 1993 when I found myself alone and frightened. I kept a journal then, but that particular book of events and emotions was all far too personal to share with anyone except myself. I can only just about read it now- it all hurt so much. This time it is different as my life has changed due to a disease which is just nobody's fault. In some ways this illness is much easier to cope with than the tragic intervention of an unemployed rock star who swept my wife away! I hope what follows is of interest to Kate, my friends and family and all that have populated my tiny empire.

"The Invasion."

Chapter One

It didn't seem worth complaining about but in March 2008 I felt like my legs had flu although everything else was all right. It was a bit of a nuisance but it didn't stop me going to work or anything else. Walking the dog and playing games of football with the boys were not so easy. I didn't believe it was worth bothering the doctor about so instead I visited a chemist shop. When I explained that I felt ill from the waist down the pharmacist said 'Come back when the rest of your body has caught up.'

This sound piece of advice kept me going for another three months before the rest of my body did eventually catch up. Typically, I felt pretty rough just as my two weeks' holiday was about to start in July. We were staying in an isolated, converted railway carriage on Pagham beach in Sussex when the high temperatures kicked in and I'm not referring to the weather. The weather was awful, by the way. Night times were worse than the day and so much fluid came out of me in the form of sweat that I felt much lighter when I staggered out of bed in the mornings. It must have been frightening for Kate and the kids, especially on the night when my phone packed in and then so did the car battery. We felt stranded that night and were glad when morning arrived. I was rarely well enough to go out that week and waited indoors as the others tried to make the best of the situation. Our second week of the holiday, intended to be spent in Cornwall, became the real casualty as we drove back home to West Yorkshire. Travelling the two hundred miles back home as safely as we could was to be a team effort - I drove for an hour, then Kate took over. Once back in Wakefield I did feel ill enough to bother a doctor. The first one I met clearly wasn't bothered about me and I left the surgery with little more advice than the pharmacist had given me four months earlier. I wonder why that is such a common experience for so many people? I made another appointment and tried again. Thankfully, the next doctor I met recognised something was seriously wrong and admitted me to a general hospital for tests.

As Kate drove me there, we still had no idea what my problem was but felt relieved that I was being taken seriously. A day or two should sort things out, I told myself. As we approached the hospital another voice, unfamiliar to me, emerged from somewhere. It was a voice that I would come to know very well during the next fourteen nights. It was telling me that something much more serious was going on than I cared to admit. I began to fear what lay ahead as we struggled to find a parking space.

Chapter 2

I have been fortunate up to now as hospital trips have usually been with the kids and involved visits to Accident and Emergency. Like most dads with four kids, I have been there about twenty times. It has been quite a good meeting place and I've rekindled several friendships there. One such visit involved my eldest son. When Sam was two years old we were at a friend's house enjoying a hot day, cold beers and a barbeque. Chatting away, I was holding Sam in the kitchen as he picked up a sharp boning knife from a clay pot jar. 'Put it down,' I suggested.

He did! He dropped it and the knife went straight through my bare foot and pinned it to the floorboards. In hospital, the casualty doctor attending to me was so tired he dressed the wrong foot! Thinking this to be amusing, I didn't inform him the foot that actually needed dressing was the one bleeding onto the floor. When the nurse pointed out his mistake he was at first apologetic but then became very annoyed with me.

Less than one year later, I recognised him on another visit to the hospital. This time I was in for a vasectomy. Despite being gowned up for this small operation, I was really concerned that he might recognise me and try to get his own back. I then asked the nurse for a pen and paper and quickly wrote him a short but formal note explaining my change of mind. I am glad I did as Michael and Joe are the products of my cowardice.

Before writing the next few paragraphs I am aware that the first part of this account won't make comfortable reading for the local hospital. I'm sure it won't be too easy to write about either. I've changed the names to protect the guilty - thankfully these were in the minority.

Once Kate and I had found a parking space at the hospital my first port of call was the medical admissions' unit. The ward's reception was surprisingly full of nurses but all were deep in conversation about a local tanning studio. I have always found it difficult being noticed at the bar of a pub and this was no different. Kate and I were both ignored. Eventually I was shown to a bed by two nurses, still talking about 'Sun Factor Express.' Next was my blood test. A nurse called Hayley tied a rubber glove tightly around the top of my arm, which looked more like a handy way to kill a chicken than an introduction to specialist care. My fears were realised when the vein seemed to burst and blood splattered all over my arm. She managed to fill only two of the four bottles required and stalked off, along with her rubber glove.

'My name is Pete by the way,' I shouted after her. She flicked me a resentful look.

Two other well-tanned nurses took over after I was informed that Hayley had gone for a break as she was tired! This time I was given a name tag and covered in blue sticky labels for heart monitoring and there I lay, feeling exposed and labelled like a bunch of ripening Fyffe's bananas. Eventually the doctor arrived and paid a lot of attention to my stomach area. He wrote quite a lot down and asked me if I had been to a tropical country lately. One week on Pagham beach was the nearest I could come up with. He nodded, tutted and left - that was all I got out of him.

To my right, Walter was admitted. A very elderly Yorkshire man, who had fallen over in his bathroom. He was obviously in shock, nor could he hear very well. The attending doctor insisted on shouting questions at him for nearly an hour. I thought a pad and pencil would have been a lot more dignified for Walter. As it was, the whole ward could hear about him, his life and his accident. 'Can you lie flat?' the doctor shouted.

'No I don't, nor do I swear, either!' Walter replied indignantly. The doctor continued to bawl, 'Have you ever had Jaundice?' I waited for the reply which was bound to be wonderfully unpredictable - and I wasn't disappointed.
'No, my Dad did, but I can't remember their names.'

I expected to hear a lot more from Walter as the night drew on.

Late into the evening Kate went home to the kids. 'Get some rest' she said. Soon afterwards I had a visitor; a man with a badly scarred face. He wore no shoes or socks and aggressively insisted that I was in his bed. He visited me three more times by midnight and each time tried to turn me out of the bed. The man to my left who had been lying silently with his back to me suddenly got up, packed his stuff, took off his shirt, sprayed a whole can of Lynx over himself (and the rest of us in the ward) put his shirt back on and left. In the next hour three different nurses, all well tanned, asked me which way he went.
'That way' I replied, while pointing to a door leading into the community. His bed was soon filled by Kevin, my new neighbour. It was now two in the morning.

'What are you reading?... What are you writing?... Do you follow Leeds?... When does the doctor come?... Am I keeping you awake?'

Kevin asked me ten other things before the nurses arrived. They all commented on the strong smell of Lynx, before asking Kevin to take his shirt off for the Fyffe's test.

'I am not one of the pretty ones,' Kevin informed them.
'Don't you worry we see some horrible things in here during a shift' said one of them tactfully.

13

Kevin, somehow reassured by this, took off his shirt and all three of the nurses fell silent. I was left to ponder what they had seen. They left him alone soon after. Poor man, he was in his fifties like me, and lived alone unlike me, but confided that he couldn't get to sleep without his Leeds United quilt. I endured his questions until three in the morning. By this time I was actually delighted to see the badly scarred man return for a fifth visit, still no shoes and still convinced that I was in his bed. I had completely forgotten that I was ill by this time.

Walter meanwhile shouted out for somebody called Jane and then as he woke he screamed out to a pair nurses passing the end of his bed 'Watch that fucking thing, it's rolling right behind you!'

They both looked behind themselves. Evidently, Walter did swear after all. The rest of the night didn't last long as there wasn't much of it left but it passed quietly enough as I lay in my bed, sweating profusely in peace. If he knew how wet my sheets were the badly scarred man wouldn't have been so keen on occupying my bed. He must have found his own eventually and Kevin just sat quietly clicking four one pound coins together. It was his taxi fare home. We hadn't got much in common, but we both wanted to go home. Me to Kate, Michael and Joe. Kevin to his matching quilt and pillow set.

In the early hours of the morning, the shifts changed over and the Sun Factor Express team were replaced by a much paler and portlier crew. They were also a great deal more friendly. Ward sister Lilly told me that I was being transferred to the 'Gastro Ward'. Bearing in mind that I still didn't know what my illness was, this news upset me a lot. A few months previously my friend and neighbour Dave had died of stomach cancer. I had known him for ten years, but his illness took him away within ten months.

14

I was now desperate for someone to say that I had nothing serious, but I was left alone with my fears and observations. There were two more of the latter on this ward before I was wheeled away.

Firstly, I was pushed past a small room and noticed two policewomen struggling with a girl aged about sixteen. She was 'off her head' with an overdose or something similar and was out of control. Her much older boyfriend was there too, looking on, shouting abuse at the police and trying to put something in her mouth. Quite a battle ensued. The second incident took place just a few yards further on. It involved the ward sister who was in a 'stand off' with the badly scarred man. He had at last found his own bed and the bottle of spirits he had hidden in it. No wonder he was trying to get me to move out of my bed earlier. Sister Lilly was now standing behind a trolley for cover and protection as she bargained with him, trying to swap the medicine he needed for the bottle of vodka. The bargaining continued as I was wheeled through the exit door.

My somewhat critical view of the medical assessment team had changed overnight. It must be hell to work there – short, ill-fated encounters with frightened and disturbed people. If I worked there I would be straight down to the tanning studio as soon as my shift was over! I was delighted to be leaving though very worried about the 'Gastro Ward' as they called it. No, not worried, I was frightened of this illness. My bones were telling me that something was seriously wrong.

Chapter Three

I soon find myself in my new ward which, I am told, is for any illnesses from the waist up! This is an odd reversal of fortunes since my visit to the pharmacy. It seems to be a safe home for my suspicious bones and I find myself in a bay of only five beds. I suddenly feel quite young as I guess that my peer group are much older, most likely in their seventies or eighties. I quickly read their names from the whiteboard above each bed: Reg, Gary, Sam and John. I am next to Gary, which is unfortunate, but near the window which is less so. He not only has a terrible cough which is constant but is also incontinent and his face is a green colour which I guess is something to do with his liver. I'll find out later.

As I settle into my space, a shock awaits me in the shape of John, who's in the bed opposite me and also by a window. He looks like my Dad and, as he tries to speak, he sounds as if he has the same illness. I thought I had coped well with Dad's illness and his recent death but looking at John proved to be an impossibility, though listening to him was unavoidable. It brings back so much emotion from the days visiting my Dad during his last, painful days in hospital. I try to block John from my field of vision and wait for Kate to arrive.

Within the next couple of hours I have spoken to them all, including John. In the furthest bed away from me is Reg, who is actually ninety two and has constipation. Strange how you can know somebody for years and never find out a thing about them. Here though, you gladly exchange intimate details with total strangers within a few minutes. His only relative has given him a mobile phone to contact her with but he doesn't know how to use it. I suddenly become quite useful, even with my lack of interest in modern communication technology.

Gary seems the most poorly with his liver problem. He insists on trying to get to the toilet on his own, but never makes it in time, I know him from somewhere I am sure. Sam is in for a blood transfusion and observation as his long standing diabetes is playing him up.

I am right about John, he has Chronic Obstructive Airways disease. Now in his seventies, he is feeling the effects of a lifetime in the mining industry. I manage to put aside my fear of listening to him cough as I know a fair bit about how he is feeling and what impact it has upon him from the experience of my Dad's illness. In fact, it turns out we get on very well. The resemblance is uncanny though and in a way it feels like Dad is here keeping me company, keeping an eye on me.

Each of my new 'bed pals' wants to know what is wrong with me but I can't help them - I just don't know. They settle for the fact that I have good hearing and better mobility than all of them put together. They also think I am quite useful and don't hesitate to ask me to visit the shop for newspapers or treats and write out their meal requests. The main function I carry out for them is to visit the sluice room, fetch urinal bottles and then to draw their curtains so they can have some privacy.

When Kate arrives I am really delighted to see her. She has left the kids at home with yet another friend and brought me some objects for my tiny empire - tape player, another friend's pyjamas (I don't own any), two books, my writing pad, fruit juice and a stack of twenty pence pieces for the phone. Each of these finds a home and I take unusual care in making sure they are all lined up tidily and accessible. We both remain confused as to why I am here and wait for the doctor. He does arrive eventually but just says I can expect to be in the ward for a couple of weeks while they carry out tests. The first of these will be tomorrow.

17

By lunchtime, I feel as if I have become officially aged seventy five. Those that can walk are informed they have to go to the day room for the mid day meal. John takes my arm for the short walk in just the same way as my Dad used to do. I had ordered a cheese omelette. Once seated, I am handed a full plate of liver and bacon, mash and dark, dark gravy which is listed as the 'leading chef's choice'. The dinner lady slapped it down shouting; 'There you are Maurice.'

Maurice, whoever he was may have ended up with my omelette on the other side of the hospital, who knows? But the meal was not even fit for my chickens at home let alone anyone in this ward needing nourishment. By night time I am beginning to understand this institutional scene - avoid the hospital tea and any hot food. I am pleased to get another visit from Kate with her lists, get well cards, sandwiches and clean clothes. She has organised a rota of visitors and it looks like every visiting time will be filled with my mates and family.

Kate looks nice too and I am reminded of the film 'Midnight Express' when the girlfriend visits her boyfriend who is serving a life sentence in a Turkish prison. For those of you who have seen it, we don't go as far as they did. It is only my second day! I have to make do with holding hands.

That is how the day works out. Not too bad, but the night time is different. I am soaked through with sweat, my body is 'popping' water for four hour sessions causing changes of clothes and sheets and preventing sleep. The night staff again are not too friendly. I feel as if I am a nuisance asking for fresh sheets and I listen to them dealing with Gary, my incontinent neighbour. Sure, he is hard work, but it isn't his fault. Comments like 'It's mucky people like you that stop us dealing with people who really need help' are hard to listen to. In an effort to help Gary, I tell the nurses before they go off shift that I have heard them speaking to him during the night. There is an improvement from then on.

As I thought, I do know Gary. He used to work in the same college as me, but not in the same section. He is keen to get out of bed and we go down to the coffee machine. Only ten minutes have passed over a plastic cup of brown liquid when he tells me what has actually happened to him. He took early retirement from college following a bereavement. His son at just 35 years old was found to have a brain tumour and died three months later. Gary retreated into his bungalow visiting the local shop for provisions and plenty of heavy duty alcohol - within eighteen months he had messed his liver up drinking whisky.

This sixty year old man is in tears as his story unfolds and it's obvious he needs some proper help, not just a chat over a cup of coffee with a comparative stranger like me. This is his first trip out of our five bedded bay and soon he feels it is time for him to return. As we walk back to the bay, he soils himself in the corridor, just ten yards away from the nearest toilet.

As usual, the next morning the consultant and his juniors visit each bed and Kate has arrived to see if there is any news, but there isn't. They move on and approach Gary in the bed next to me. We share a synthetic curtain, okay for privacy, but no use for keeping out smells and sounds. I hear Gary tell the doctor that he is suffering from the loss of his son and that he is drinking too much. This seems like real progress to me. Kate and I wait for an appropriate response from the consultant but he skirts over Gary's revelation with 'But you are very ill, is there anything we can do for you now?'
'Fetch me a loaded gun' comes Gary's reply.

Chapter 4

It has been a while now since I have had any real sleep. Gary is partly to blame but these sweats I am getting are ruthless in their regularity; midnight until 4.00am without fail. That is probably the reason the 'night demons' visit me and stay until it gets light. They plague me and it proves impossible to get rid of the thoughts and phrases they leave me with:

This is cancer.... hard luck! You haven't got long.... you can't sort things out lying here.... shame you won't see those boys grow up. You left a banana in your office desk.... Not a bad life was it.... You still owe the coalman £65.... Should be a decent size funeral.... Never got to India, did you?... Could have done more.

I am not really sure what brings the demons but if I drift off they whisper about me amongst themselves until I wake again, then I join in. Long conversations about the consequences of a terminal illness. My imagination needs a remote control so I can change the channel, volume and light. The daylight does at last arrive and brings me some sense of perspective after all, it could be anything that is making me ill. The nurse weighs me again this morning. At ten stone four I am six pounds lighter than yesterday.

The tests that follow are over a five day period and include body scans, marrow bone tests and an ultra sound scan. The doctor informs me that the marrow bone test can be uncomfortable. Nothing unusual about this I thought. How wrong I was. A very kind nurse called Emma, holds my hand while the procedure is carried out. They give me a local sedative, but really I need a bit of driftwood to bite on.

It really does hurt and I am very grateful to Emma for being so kind. I am promised the results fairly quickly but they are delayed by the August Bank Holiday weekend.

Three more days and nights to lie waiting. The prospect of this is very hard to cope with though the days are easy in comparison to the nights. Kate always arrives at the early visiting time and friends or family in the evening. However, the least welcome visitors come later at night without any regard for the visiting hours.

The bank holiday weekend though only three days, seems like a fortnight and gives the night demons a chance for more gossip. A long weekend keeps them very interested. The ringleader gets me down most of all, hiding under the bed until everyone is gone and then gathering up all of his mates. Only once did they fail to visit. Keeping them away for that night was a proud achievement - I was still awake sweating, but they didn't come and pester me.

I remember ringing Kate at seven in the morning to tell her they hadn't been. I am so proud of myself that I am in tears on the phone. Kate must have been in the middle of school uniforms, breakfast for the boys and a dog walk but understands why I have rung. She sounds tired and upset - maybe the little sods had been to visit her instead of me. If that is the case then I am relieved when they come back to spend the remaining nights with me.

Chapter 5

I spend a lot of time with mates, I visit them, have them round for a meal, work alongside them and play next to them. Some I see regularly, some not so, but I am pretty good at keeping in touch with them. Unfortunately for them, I am the sort of bloke that staggers into a phone box on leaving the pub, regardless of the time and rings up a mate to say how much I love him! I don't do that so much nowadays, not because I don't want to; it's just really hard finding a phone box. Despite that kind of behaviour, it still comes as quite a shock when you see all of those friends within a space of two weeks. I had no idea that so many people would push the turnstile and visit my tiny space in this hospital.

My friends live all over the country so there was a fair bit of travelling going on - from Windermere, Newquay, North Yorkshire and one old friend drives up all the way from Lands End in a fifteen year old Mazda! Some stay the night in a hotel near the hospital, some stay with Kate for the night. As a result of all these visits my tiny empire soon needs to find spaces and places for magazines, biscuits, books, story and music tapes. The tapes are a rescue, especially at night. I am still sweating and losing weight, but it is harder for those demons to break through, especially when I'm involved in a story tape or listening to Paul Rogers singing his way through 'The Free Story:'

Help me to repay, things I have done wrong,
Help me find a way, to get where I belong,
All I can say, when I'm feeling this way
Is to buy me some time
And a little happiness some day.

Back at home Kate was also getting a lot of help and support from local friends, her own family who travelled from Ireland and those more local from the school and the church. Sometimes the biggest help came from people whom we hardly knew! Cards and 'rescue packages' appeared all the time. One from my sister contained chocolate for the kids, wine and whisky for us and even our dog received some treats.

Anyone reading will know that when things are going wrong, there is usually something brilliant that materialises. You remember that time when you were broken down on a country road and a stranger appeared with a huge torch, a flask of something hot and a tow rope! All of that arrived in the form of kindness, support and love from all of the people I know or work with. That is what kept me going despite all of the medical routines, the observations, the tests, the needles and the blood transfusions that were now my new companions. Whatever the single reason or force behind this illness, it was transformed by so many people helping in so many different ways. When just a bit of sunshine hits a crystal, the room can be covered in colour and that is how it felt. The dark and scary nights were easier to cope with knowing that I would have company the next day.

I am still waiting for the tests though and it is taking forever. The main diagnosis is to be discovered by studying a small gland that I have removed from my neck. It didn't take much to cut it out, just a general anaesthetic and a two inch scar, but the result is to take seven days in the laboratory. I feel that the ward sister, Brenda really knows what is the matter with me but she doesn't say anything as the junior doctors deliberate over my poorly self. (When I met her months later in the hospital car park, we spoke about that time and I was right, she did know all along!)

The distraction from waiting for the results this day is the visit from my kids. Sam and Rosie are back from college, so are keen to come. Kate brings Michael and Joe during the day. I am worried about their reaction to seeing me but needn't have been. We sit in the day room and throw paper aeroplanes about. They don't ask much, just seem to be satisfied that I am still kicking about. Conversation is just about the usual things like football and the stuff they are doing to keep busy in the school holidays. The visit doesn't seem to last long, just an hour, but makes me long to be back at home for even half of that time.

As Kate gathers up all the paper planes she leaves me with a card for the next day. In the twelve years we have been married, I have always managed to remember our anniversary but this time I had no idea what the date is and have nothing to give her in return.

Sam, my eldest is an 'arty type' and studying sculpture in Bath. Rosie is training to be a Speech Therapist in Leicester. Sam is taller than me and leaner. He reminds me of Heathcliff from Wuthering Heights. He also used to throw paper aeroplanes about, but now has a style of his own. Rosie is much more like me in personality though I must concede, much bonnier. I can tell she is upset. More tears are restrained than on show and we get through the visit well enough. Now they have left home they have a lot of adventures and learn things that you can't teach them at home so there is a lot to talk about.

Before they leave I manage to fashion an anniversary card for Kate from a piece of writing paper. It is just a daft drawing of me in hospital and some words that I really feel to be the truth. I give it to Sam to deliver next day. If I had given it to Rosie, then I would be sure she would deliver it. For some reason I entrust it to Sam, it is an important job and I wanted him to take the responsibility for it.

When I speak to Kate on the phone the next morning, she has received my makeshift card. We are apart but still feel together.

I leave the phone and go to a little bathroom that I have recently discovered in the corridor. Nobody else uses it because there is no lock on the door. As the water fills the sink I let out a huge wave of despair and sob uncontrollably. Sinks are a great place to break down in, this was my third such sink. I clearly remember the other two which acted as hosts for my sorrow the year my wife left us. People think you are washing up and there is only a possible reflection in a window that can give you away. This lonely bathroom became a little bolt hole for me. Five or ten minutes in there and I come out a bit braver and without any whiskers after a quick shave.

So a sad little chapter in many ways, waiting for news that doesn't come and still fearing the worst, still thinking about what had happened to my mate, Dave. After two weeks and none the wiser, I am allowed home to await the results of my neck biopsy. I am pleased to be going home but oddly with some genuine reluctance I pack away the contents of my tiny empire. I say good bye to my new mates and to the tiny space where my friends and family have visited so regularly - a space where I had received so much kindness that it was sometimes difficult to deal with. I had no idea that so many people would be so keen to see me get better.

Chapter 6

Only three days are spent at home before a phone call comes through from the consultant's secretary. The night demons haven't followed me home, but the sweats and high temperatures do. It becomes easiest for me to put a mattress down on the floor at the end of our bed, covered in towels for my night shift. I have stopped losing so much weight too, but am now two stones lighter than before I went into hospital. The secretary gives me an appointment for the following day but, of course, she gives me no suggestion as to what the doctor will say. Kate and I will have to drive in to see him in the morning. More waiting!

The next day. It is time for the waiting to finish and it does. On arrival at the hospital, Kate and I are ushered into a room which has two vases containing real flowers, a leather settee and three chairs. We are then offered a cup of tea which arrives and is a actually a decent 'cuppa'. This must be serious. The tension builds as the doctor arrives and introduces an experienced nurse who sits quietly in one of the chairs. Is she there to sedate me or arouse me from a faint following the news? Kate and I hold hands. More sweating, this time for a different reason.

He lists the problems and the various things found out from tests. I had found out about problems with my liver, spleen, lumps, bumps and blood disorders one by one over a couple of weeks, but when they are all put together in a sentence it sounds as if I am in for the kind of result that my demons had predicted:

'You have Hodgkin's Lymphoma' he states.

A brief explanation reveals it is cancer of the lymphatic system.

My lymphocytes have turned cancerous and become 'lymphomas'. Who knows why? It is quite a rare disease and therefore difficult to diagnose. About two people in every 100,000 get it every year. I must have had it quite a while as it is now at an advanced stage. It is a shock, but Kate and I are managing it rather stoically as we sit on the leather settee. Good news does eventually arrive from the doctor's lips as I am listening to the information he gives: Hodgkin's Lymphoma has about a 70% recovery rate for someone of my age but I will need at least six months of chemotherapy. Relief is greater than shock and I can't concentrate on anything else he has to say. Just one thought is repeating in my head:

It's not fatal, just serious, not fatal, just serious, not fatal...............

This may just become the most crucial journey of my life but, at the same time, I now feel it will be a journey that won't necessarily claim my life. Nevertheless, I have just been invaded.

"Occupation"

Chapter 7

It was in truth a little difficult to understand this cancer. There was no tumour to treat, nothing to cut off and it seemed to be quite rare, so it wasn't going to be easy to meet somebody else who had been through similar treatment. After the doctor left the leather settee, we then found out a lot more from the nurse who had been sitting in with us. Sister Laura, as she introduced herself, spent over an hour with us and was very, very helpful. She informed us both about all sorts of issues - how the weeks ahead might shape up, about talking to our children and how the chemotherapy would be expected to work.

There was a lot to take in but she also had a booklet for us on the disease and some other literature about speaking to the kids so we could go over it all at home. I liked her and thought that she would prove to be really important over the coming year. She told us that she could tell by the way Kate and I were reacting to the news that we would be all right. I looked at Kate sitting beside me. I could tell she was being brave about this and looking after me, I was doing exactly the same for her. Sister Laura had made a good assessment.

In the car on the way home, little was said between us, I just flicked through the booklet and kept looking at an appointment date to start my chemotherapy. The car radio was on - *'Everybody Hurts'* by REM. Kate concentrated on the motorway. I looked out at the industrial units scattered along the M62, I had never looked at them in such detail before but the closer examination just rendered them more dreary than ever. What was I expecting on the M62? A neon sign above the motorway with a bright message saying, 'You'll be all right Pete. Just hang in there.' That would have done nicely.

Chapter 8

The following couple of evenings were spent giving news to family and friends. Each phone call was different as each person I spoke to were offering support or help in whatever way they could. Most of all, I tried to explain my feelings of relief that, at last, I knew what had been causing all these symptoms. It was specific and treatable with a high rate of success, even though the cancer was quite advanced.

On the second night at home, I sat in bed and read the booklets Sister Laura had given us. They showed Hodgkin's Lymphoma to have certain identifying features: night sweats, loss of weight, extreme fatigue and high temperatures. I was a classic case! I wondered why it had taken so long to find out what was wrong with me. I read too about the chemotherapy that had been prescribed. It is called A.B.V.D. which is an abbreviation for the four drugs involved; Adriamycin, Bleomycin, Vinblastin and Dacarbazine and I had been told it was a tough regime, in truth I had no idea. I was to take them through the veins in my hand every fortnight. I had been told to expect a minimum of twelve treatments and a maximum of sixteen.

It was hard to get to sleep after all that and, just for a change, I was quite relieved when the night sweats grabbed hold of me again. I usually dreaded them, but they gave me something to do. Four more hours of activity back on the mattress at the end of the bed with more towels and more of my mate's pyjamas. I had no idea what lay ahead really or how it might affect me as an individual. All I did know was that I needed to buy some pyjamas of my own and I felt miserable. About 3am I found my way into the bathroom and weighed myself just to add to the agony. Still two stones lighter than three weeks ago. Here was my fourth sink. Another bloody good sob.

Chapter 9

Sam and Rosie came to understand what was happening through the hospital visits and keeping up with news. It was difficult for them but they were able to read the booklets about Hodgkins Lyphoma. They asked a dozen different questions. I answered about three of them with some accuracy.

For Michael and Joe it was different. They were already hearing things at school. Most of the parents were really helpful but a grim few were more intrigued about what was going on and gossiping at the school gate. Joe, the youngest, told me one of the kids in his class had asked if his Dad had cancer. Later I found Michael looking at a picture in his 'Guinness Book of Records' of the largest tumour ever removed from a human - it was time to sort this out as best I could. I managed to clarify two useful points for them.

Firstly I taught them the meaning of three words - *'terminal'*, *'manageable' and 'treatable.'*. 'Terminal' explained that it was a cancer which would cause somebody to die sooner or later. 'Manageable' implied that it was a cancer that might not be cured, but the patient could live a long time. 'Treatable' meant that it was a cancer that could be cured completely. Once they had fixed these three words clearly in their minds I was able to explain that Hodgkin's was a 'treatable' type. Several weeks later I was passing Joe's bedroom, as he and his friend Ben were playing Lego.
'Why has your Dad's hair come out?' asked Ben as he added another brick to the spaceship.
'He's got Hodgkin's Disease,' Joe replied, 'but it's treatable.'

The second explanation came much later on when I was very poorly from the effects of chemotherapy. This involved a story book called

'The Mousehole Cat' - a smashing children's book. If you haven't read it, the story is about the Cornish village of Mousehole - a fishing village hiding behind a sea wall which uses a tiny exit from the harbour into the sea, hence 'the mouse hole.' There is a prolonged storm and the village begins to starve as no fishing boat can leave the harbour. At the height of the tempest, Old Tom braves the storm with his cat, Mowzer. The illustrations in the book show a huge 'storm cat' playing with the boat until Mowzer sings to calm him. Tom, meanwhile, casts his nets and makes his escape back to the village, complete with his catch.

The boys seemed to understand that the medicine I needed was just like the 'storm cat' playing with the boat and, to become better I had to get out and face something that I was frightened of. Some people would help me and ease the pain just like the cat's singing did. In the end the catch would be worth all the danger.

It isn't easy breaking news about cancer to anyone - friends or family and especially children. The reaction from most people is understandable. They are often not quite sure what to say. On one occasion after telling a friend over the phone that I couldn't play golf because I had picked up a cancer, he replied, 'Really? I was thinking of missing this week myself, I've got got a stiff neck.'

For someone in my position there was at least that one single sensible message; it was reminding me that I could have had a diagnosis that was so much worse: '*It's not fatal. Just serious*'. I tried to keep those four words at the beginning of every conversation I undertook with a worried friend or member of the family. Secretly, I feared that my children may lose me to this disease and these fears surfaced mostly during the hours I spent alone at night, awake and sweating. Bizzarely, on one such night I gave up the idea of sleeping and stole quietly downstairs where I wrote to each one of

31

the children. I sat at our dining table to carry out the task with a writing pad and a fountain pen. My body was 'popping' beads of sweat as I deliberated long and hard over each message. I then hid the notes in places around our rambling house, places that were not often visited, places where the notes would be found - eventually. They were short notes and designed to encourage the children with their individual talents as they faced a future without me. Those dark hours when everyone else in the house was peacefully asleep left me feeling desperate and pessimistic.

The light of the following morning, the chaos of pre-school breakfast and an argument about a lost homework file somehow rekindled the natural optimist in me. Once alone in the house, I revisited all of the hiding places and gathered up the four notes that I had written during the night. Before ripping them into pieces I read each one again. I then promised myself that I would see each one of the children develop their individual talents as they grew older and that I would be there to encourage them in person.

Chapter 10

From then on I was set on tram lines as I had no control over which direction to take. I had to sit tight, do what I was told and hope that the journey went in the right direction. My first trip out was to a mobile scanner set within the grounds of a hospital on the other side of Leeds. I had been informed that this appointment would take two or three hours, so I followed their advice and took some music with me - Paul Rogers, this time singing with 'Bad Company'. I was to experience or undergo a procedure called a PET scan which would give my consultant an accurate picture of the cell activity causing my illness. A friend of ours called Norman met us at the hospital. He had kindly driven from Wakefield to Pontefract Hospital and then onto Leeds to pick up a DVD we needed for the scan. We hadn't known Norman and his wife Louise very long and this was the first of many things they did for us during the coming months. I was the first patient of the day and after filling in a form I was led out to a lorry trailer which transports this rare and expensive scanning machine around venues in the North of England.

The trailer contained three units - a preparation room, control centre and scanner. In the first room I was given a bright red radioactive dye which was produced from something that looked like a nuclear safe. After the injection, I was left alone in this tiny place for an hour, surrounded by lead-encased walls and feeling extremely claustrophobic. Next time, I must remember to bring a book I thought. However, the hour dragged past eventually and I was released from that leaden prison and escorted to a toilet by a nurse who apologised for walking five yards in front of me due to the fact that I was now radioactive. I was so nervous I couldn't use the toilet. It had a sign on the door:

Toilet For The Use Of Radioactive Patients Only' - with the appropriate diagram.

Even if I had been able to ignore this, I soon had that familiar feeling (for us blokes) when you are using the loo at work and needing 'to go'. Suddenly, your boss appears next to you. The urge to have a wee disappears, though his doesn't. He may even pass a confident remark, making the situation much worse. (Just to be clear, I know all bosses aren't men. My present boss is a woman. Now, Andrea has surprised me in several ways but has never, to date, appeared next to me in a urinal!)

I left the toilet and, in front of the 'radioactive' sign and fifteen people awaiting an X-ray, had to inform the nurse of my failure to perform. She smiled sympathetically and informed me the scan would be more successful if I managed to relieve myself. She escorted me back to the trailer, this time ten yards ahead. She turned her head and informed me: 'Be sure you don't meet any pregnant women or children for the next six hours.'

During the one hundred yards walking back to the lorry, I considered this. I really did feel that I was a danger to the local population. Just turning a corner and bumping into a child could ruin its future. The PET scanner soon emerged into view and I sped up the steps before I could do any damage to the child-rearing community. Back in the confines of the lead cased trailer, I was ushered into the scanner room and invited to drop my trousers to my ankles, remove my wedding ring and climb onto the machine. If she had given me this advice the other way around it would have made the ascent a little more dignified. After an uncomfortable struggle, I decided to take my trousers right off, feeling far better in socks and pants. I thought the scanner looked scary enough without adding to my humiliation. Once in position my head was placed firmly into a foam restraining clamp and I was invited to lie still for the next hour. Before the nurse left me, I asked her to play my Bad Company CD which would last fifty minutes and carry me through most of the next hour's session. She took it, left the room, pressed a locking door button and took a position at her viewing window alongside the PET scanner technician.

By raising my eyes as far as my static head would allow, I looked behind me at the scanner while waiting for the platform to kick into action and move through the machine. I had feared that it would be a long tube or pod like structure, like you might see in a Japanese hotel, so I was relieved to see that it wasn't like that. It was similar to a huge Polo mint, about a metre in depth, through which my body would pass. The claustrophobic feeling that I had experienced in the preparation room returned as the lights on the machine came on and I started to move. However, any panic was under control at least for now – the thought foremost in my mind was that I needed a wee – desperately!

The best way to get through this was to think of holidays that I had enjoyed and, for some reason, old girlfriends. That accounted for about five minutes - fifty five to go (minutes not girlfriends.) Where was my music? Actually, I did well for the next half hour by closing my eyes and identifying the colours that I could see. Purple was the predominant one. I tried to avoid thinking about the seriousness of my disease as its extent was being illustrated to the technician viewing his monitor. The last twenty minutes were much worse. I could feel panic setting in, my bladder was bursting and any humorous reflections drained away like water down a plug hole leaving me still, exposed and very frightened.

Just as I was about to raise my hand and shout my surrender, the door unlocked automatically and, over the intercom came a nurse's voice telling me to sit, get dressed and put my shoes on.

35

This time the advice came in the right order. Luckily, I remembered the wedding ring myself. Another movie clip raised itself from my memory bank by association. It was the one featuring Jack Nicholson in 'One Flew Over The Cuckoo's Nest.' It is the scene when he has been subjected to Electric Shock Therapy for bad behaviour and limps back into the ward pretending to be a zombie. I must have looked like that, I certainly felt like it. Though wobbly, I asked,. 'What happened to my music?'
'Sorry about that. We couldn't figure out how to work the CD player!'

As I staggered down the steps, looking now less keenly for children and pregnant women, I realised that I had just gone through nearly three hours of advanced technology, administered by highly trained technicians in a lorry that must have cost a couple of million pounds, yet nobody had been capable of putting the CD player on! However, only another two hundred yards of child dodging before I could relieve myself in the 'Radioactive Only' toilet and my experience was over. This time I could have shared the loo with Osama Bin Laden - it would have made no difference. Relief!

Chapter 11

I wasn't too worried about the results of the PET scan, I knew that I had Hodkgin's Disease, now it was just about identifying the stage and the treatment. The scans and tests during the two weeks in hospital had been far more scary in terms of awaiting a diagnosis. Of greater concern was catching something as this disease effects the immune system. You have to take your temperature regularly and avoid places where there are lots of people. It all gets a bit complicated and the night sweats make you seem ill, but it's just part of the deal. Catching something can be serious. For example, imagine getting through all the cancer treatment just to lose out to pneumonia or septicaemia.

My first scare came just a few days before my chemotherapy was due to start. I was really hot and unwell with a temperature at around 39 degrees and about to ring the hospital. Suddenly, Kate flew in the door and collapsed on the settee. I felt her head and she was freezing, so were her hands and fingers. This, along with the terrible stomach pain she was experiencing, called for some action. I thought briefly about a dinner I had eaten a while back when I had received a starter of hot lettuce and cold bacon which didn't seem right. This was even worse, with me boiling up and Kate at the opposite end of the scale, I piled some blankets on her and made her a hot water bottle. I then rang the doctor who promised a visit sometime that afternoon.

I couldn't think of anything else I could do except put the kettle on and try to keep her calm. Just then the man with a flashlight, tow rope and hot flask arrived. Norman and Louise, both nurses, turned up on a social call and were confronted by the scene I have described. Before long we were both calm, more settled and, to some extent, enjoying the visit as they had intended. The next caller was the doctor who soon identified the problem as a panic attack. By now, Kate was feeling warmer and had regained her usual temperature. She was left with a prescription for some tablets and started to come round. As the doctor left I felt shocked that my illness was having such an effect on those around me. It was a surprising event. I always have been a touch on the niaive side. A month had now passed since our holiday in Pagham and we had been through such a lot in a short time. The next six months were going to throw all sorts at us, I was sure of that, though not at all sure what those things would be.

Chapter 12

With my temperature still soaring, we eventually phoned the local hospital in the evening and set off to see what was the matter with me. Michael and Joe were in bed by this time and one of our neighbours came over to mind them both until we returned. However, only Kate did. The staff on this ward took some tests and observations and before I knew it I was admitted and attached to a drip for fluids. My first infection returned me to my tiny empire but, this time surrounded by four men all with cancers of one type or another. Conversation wasn't so easy, but the most noticeable factor for me was the ward itself. Compared to those I had been in before - it was lovely! I mean it was really clean, bright, spacious and seemed well staffed.

I mentioned my Dad earlier. He ended his time on a general ward suffering from a lung condition which restricted his breath. He used to say to me, 'Those bloody cancer patients, they get the lot!' I never asked him how he knew this but he was right and how glad I am for it. The nurses looked after me so well during the night with a regular change of bed linen and towels to cope with my night sweating. In the morning a caterer approached me and asked what I would like for breakfast! Later on, I was offered my own DVD player, complete with television, on a trolley that came right up to my bed. I watched a long film called 'Atonement' before lunch which was hot and tasty. By now, I had managed some chat with my neighbouring bed pal who was a regular visitor to this ward due to infections. He confirmed my Dad's suspicions too and we spoke for a while about the differences between the general wards and this oncology unit. Just like my bacon and lettuce 'starter', it didn't seem right.

The next day the visiting doctor recommended a blood transfusion for me. Two full bags of it. I was hot and worried and actually asked the nurse if I could be given some of the blood I had donated at the local town hall some five years ago. She really thought I was joking!.... It was quite frightening having your first blood transfusion. It took four hours as I watched someone else's blood going into my system, during this time I asked myself lots of questions, all of them based upon ignorance.

'Who was he.... do I have a blood brother.... or maybe a sister.... where do they live.... where does it all go.... is there room for it.... is my new relative an American.... will it change the way I think..... have they sorted out the aids problem?

It was on my third day in hospital that my chemotherapy treatment was due but I was in the wrong place. I was meant to be attending a day unit about ten miles away with Sister Laura and my Consultant and the brown leather seats. Despite the antibiotics I was receiving, my temperature was still high and it was decided that I should have my first treatment on this ward. The ward sister told me the treatment would be at 3pm. Awaiting that allotted time was as nerve-racking as anything that has ever happened to me in my lifetime and it was only really at this point that I came to realise an inescapable fact. Despite the symptoms, the scans, the biopsy, the results, the leaflets and the appointments, it still hadn't occurred to me that I had cancer. In the hours waiting for the chemotherapy trolley to arrive, I tried to watch another film, just something lighthearted, it made no impression upon me as I just couldn't concentrate. Each trolley I heard rattling around from 2pm onwards I thought would be the one. Mine arrived eventually nearer 4pm. It was silver, with lots of drawers and lying on the top were some bags of fluid. These were brown in colour so you couldn't see into them. The only thing the trolley didn't have was the big sign looped over the end stating 'Pete, believe it now. You've got cancer.'

It would make sense to believe that everyone who receives chemotherapy reacts to the prospect in a different way. In no way would I want to suggest that it is an experience too frightening to contemplate, but it was for me. Two nurses ignored me as they went through the serious act of checking the contents of each bag, ticked the drugs against the list and signed their names to prove they had done it. A charge nurse called Michael was to administer the medicine and there were to be four main drugs plus some other stuff to help with sickness. He was very reassuring, professional and adopted a very clinical attitude which was just what I needed. Any kindness at this point would have been too much to cope with. I was very surprised by how long the treatment took - about five hours through a drip into a vein on my hand. The charge nurse would stay with me for short periods during this time and then leave to do other jobs when he felt things were going steadily. Of the four drugs I received, by far the worst was the last one. It took ages and caused a burning pain inside my arm so the drip had to be slowed down. Despite the relationship that grew over these hours, he insisted on calling me 'sir' to which I responded 'Call me Pete, please. I can't have somebody who is helping to save my life call me 'sir'.

Late into that evening just as my treatment was over two friends visited me - Ann and Andy. I wasn't very sure about how I was reacting as I still felt very hot but I was very pleased to see them. They intended to visit Kate on the way home just to see how she was also. They hadn't been there too long, probably just a few minutes, when Ann asked why I was shaking. I got into bed fearing a chill, but the shakes became worse. By the time Ann had fetched a nurse to my bed my body was almost uncontrollable.

41

It was like having a fit really but I was awake and doing all I could to stop the convulsions. Every part of me was bouncing around, from my head to my feet. I remember hearing the bed actually crashing around and lifting off the floor slightly. I told Andy it must be nearly twenty years since I managed to move a bed that vigorously. We tried to make the best of it as you can tell. I asked Ann for a drink of tea which always help in a crisis. She ignored this very English response to an emergency and chose a cold drink for me instead, which was very wise of her. She held my wildly vibrating face to the still cup in her hand, the result was inevitable.

What a visit it was for them! In between shakes I was horribly sick and they helped me fill three disposable grey cardboard bowls. After a half an hour, which seemed to last at least sixty minutes, the nurses decided that I would need some drugs to help me through the post-chemotherapy reaction. Whatever it was they gave me left me still, but exhausted. I just about remember that I had a craving for some cold orange juice. Despite his bad knee, Andy set off to find some and it took him over thirty minutes. By then I was in a semi state of consciousness. They eventually left the ward to visit Kate on their way home but how pleased I was that they had been there with me through that experience. Had I been alone with just a set of drawn curtains for company, the impact of that first treatment would have lived with me forever.

I'll never forget their kindnesses or the taste of that cold orange juice. I am sure I will never forget how awful that seemingly simple visit must have been for them. Despite the violent event that was unfolding in front of them, they even managed to convince me that the convulsions were to be expected and that I had no need to worry. What good souls - I watched them leave the ward when the time for all visitors to leave arrived. As they moved past all of the beds in my bay and turned the corner moving out of sight I could do nothing else but relive the last hour and focus upon the care and friendship that they had given so naturally. If only they could know how much I loved them for going through all that with me, it was a turning point in my struggle to survive this storm.

Later that evening as I came round, a young nurse settled me down for the night. I had been hoping for one of the doctors or nurses to give me a few words of comfort based upon their experience. This nurse, was unqualified, on her first placement from University and went to school with my daughter. However, I don't think I will ever forget the impact of what she said and the words she uttered

'I hope you have a better night. It's not nice cancer, but of all the ones there are to have, yours is the nicest.'

I got off to sleep like a new born baby.

Chapter 13

Despite the night-time four hour sweat, the previous day's chemotherapy and the loss of appetite, I actually felt fine. My temperature had returned to normal and I was munching through a lunch brought in by Jill, an old friend of mine, as Kate arrived. I was pleased to be told I could go home and we once again tidied the contents of my tiny empire into a carrier bag. I said good bye to the patients that surrounded me but, this time I felt I would be seeing them again either here, in Pontefract, or at the clinic. I was part of a club that nobody cared to be in. My first chemotherapy treatment was proof that I was a bona fide member; I was new to this club compared to those around me but a definite and fully subscribed brother.

The only concern I had really, as Kate drove home, was the feeling at the very core of my stomach. It felt like the size of a tennis ball and it was telling me something though I couldn't quite hear the message due to the sound of the car and the conversation with Kate. Later, as I lay on top of my bed, it came through loud and clear. It was the chemotherapy, it had huddled into my stomach and said; 'Feeling alright at the moment aren't you? Just wait on a bit until I've got myself settled, then you'll see.' With that it snuggled down a bit further into my stomach. It was getting comfortable.

There had been many times when I had been laying down listening to thoughts and voices, and this was just another and I didn't like it. I left my bed just ten minutes after getting into it and joined in with the preparation for the evening meal. I prepared myself for the phone calls which would come through at regular intervals all evening. Phone calls and cards, so many people keen to know how I was. They were all worrying and each of them needed to know what had been going on. The cards were so much easier to deal with: you can open them when you want and the messages of support are heartfelt and reassuring, sometimes amusing. Joe and his friend Ben had drawn me a picture. On the front of their card, I was in bed, watching football on TV as the commentator shouted 'Middlesbrough two, Liverpool one!' The actual result this season was the other way around, thanks to a 94th minute 'screamer' from Gerrard. It was a great card and must have taken some doing, especially for Ben as he's the Liverpool fan.

The phone calls are a different issue. Each call is genuine and needs as much attention as the next but collectively they are very wearing. Kate went on phone duty and I went to bed at 10pm and prepared my mattress and towels. If I could get two hours sleep before the sweat shift kicked in then the next day would be easier. As usual, that is what happened, though I still had that strange feeling in my stomach, I had the notion that the next day might not be as comfortable.

Trying to explain what the post chemotherapy experience is like is quite difficult. I have done quite well in explaining the 'comfortable stage' so I'll try to widen the experience. It was the next day when the lump in my stomach decided on a change and that it was time to start work on me. It began by making me feel sick. This wasn't to be like the sickness you get from a tummy bug or even that type you get after finding and sharing a bottle of gin with your kid brother in the sixties. This type was to last three days. Probably the only relief from the sensation was actually being sick. The time in between vomitting saw me lying on my back in bed, swearing profusely at the invasion which had begun to take on the personality of an intruder in my body. In fact, it felt like an alien, buried deep in there somewhere, trying to eat its way out very slowly. That's not a bad description and that is how it felt for me.

It made me realise that the nursing skills required to help someone like myself get through this must be extremely specialised. The trouble was, of course, that the nurses I needed were busy elsewhere in hospital giving the medicine to somebody else. They surely couldn't have much idea about the impact the treatment has upon the patient at home and upon the family that do the caring. Perhaps they should, perhaps they have. In the meantime Kate just had to find the skills of patience, care and endurance beyond anything else she had ever experienced.

I didn't manage to sleep. In the end, we just hung on together in the dark. Two, completely alone and clueless people. Me helping her just a little bit, she helping me a lot more than that.

Chapter 14

Once the nausea had passed, I felt desperate to get out, even if it was just down the road. Luckily, I live in a place where shops, pub and post office are all within a very convenient walking distance. However, there were one or two side-effects which made walking quite painful. I can leave these to your imagination. It was quite an effort to dispel these agonies and in doing so I hadn't understood how confused I was feeling. My first port of call was a café just around the corner where I ordered and drank a milky coffee. Further on down the hill, I popped into the Co-op then entered the butcher's and joined the queue. I wanted to cook us a meal that evening, but wasn't at all sure as to what it should be. Julie, who works in the butchers, served me two gammon fillets, they were the special offer of the day. That would be enough for all of us, I thought. As she took my £2.80, Julie remarked that the gammon fillets would go down well with cauliflower cheese.

Just around the corner, in the greengrocer I had a good chat with the shop owner. Somehow he knew all about my being ill and told me how his sister-in-law had just recovered from breast cancer. I bought a cauliflower.
'There's nothing like a bit of gammon and some cheese to go with that', came his helpful advice. This seemed like a good idea to me. Within a few minutes I had gone back to Julie in the butchers and asked for some gammon.

'You daft bugger, you've got two bits in your carrier bag already, what's up with thee?'

I slowly walked back up the hill considering the circle of events that had just occurred. When I had limped to the top of the hill I bumped into the café owner who was out posting a letter.

'I am glad to see you,' he said. 'You owe me £1.50 for the coffee, just left without paying, you did!'

I paid him by the post box and he disappeared into the post office. As I paid up, I realised that I had dropped a fiver, probably at the till in the Co-op. A quick visit back there, but no fiver had been handed in. There was a notice board offering free advertising to customers with a pen and blank cards available. I left an advert:

Lost £5.00 note in this shop today. Please phone Pete. - £10.00 reward.

My first chemotherapy treatment and the immediate aftermath of it was over. Only eleven more to go.

Chapter 15

In 'chemo' language, a cycle for me was two lots of medicine and in my treatment plan, there were six cycles. I managed to avoid infection by evading crowds or groups during the next week. This meant no trips to pubs, school assemblies or church. I had to keep away from anybody with a cold or illness and hope nobody sneezed over me while I was queuing up for stamps. This meant I could have my next lot of medicine back on the day unit with Sister Laura and the ward with brown leather seats, the home of my consultant, Dr. Wright.

I felt much happier about the prospect of going in as an outpatient, thus avoiding hospital admission each time. Before the next visit to hospital we were visited by Kate's Mum and Dad who came over to help with the kids all the way from South West Cork. We were very pleased to see them again. Stella is very good at keeping Michael and Joe occupied and Bill just fits in with whatever is going on. I remember when my eldest lad, Sam, was about five years old - he met Bill for the first time and said something that made me feel a bit embarrassed.

'Bill's hair is completely white and he's not even dead yet!'

He wasn't bothered about it at all, thought it was a hoot. It has been like that ever since. It was just as well that they feel at ease whatever the scene that confronts them as there were quite a few surprises in store for them during their short stay.

My next treatment was two days away on the Wednesday but on Monday I had to go for a blood test to make sure I was strong enough for the medicine. My results were low so, at the hospital I was given an injection that would boost the activity within my bone marrow and create more white blood cells. It was just an injection in my stomach. I would need to go back for another injection on Tuesday. No trouble. I went to bed that night and as usual prepared my towels but in the middle of my predictable 'sweat shift' I developed a back pain. I have heard people complain of back ache but have been lucky enough not to have suffered, until now. The base of my spine started throbbing in rhythm with my pulse and became continuously worse until the end of one pain joined up with the beginning of the next. In fear of keeping Kate awake, I tried to get down the stairs but by then I could hardly move, it took me an age to find the painkillers in the medicine cupboard - for all the good they did.

It eased off a little in the morning but grew worse again as we drove into hospital the next day. After another blood test and another injection, I tried to leave the ward but made little progress down the long corridor. I was in tears by this time and the nurse in charge, Nanette, was lovely to me, finding me a wheelchair and with that I was able to leave. Another painful night ahead. By Wednesday, I felt absolutely 'knackered' but the back pain had gone.

Above all, I didn't want to miss a treatment; with at least eleven to go it would have filled me with despair to have fallen at the second fence. My blood test on the ward showed the injections had done their job and I had enough white blood cells for the treatment to go ahead. This became the pattern over the coming months. A treatment, then the reaction, some rest, a blood test, an injection, another one and then the treatment again. In a few short words, it all sounds easy enough to cope with. In reality it was very different. The alien within saw to that.

Chapter 16

My third treatment began at the day unit. I did admire how that small team of nurses set about their work. During the day I would meet about a dozen people who came in for their treatment. Some were in for a short time, some were in for a couple of hours, a few of us were in all day. Each of us would sit in a 'Shackleton' type of chair which were arranged into an oval shape around the room, making it easy for us to talk to one another.. It was pretty heavy going, but Sister Claire and Sister Laura knew their business. They made it feel like a social club somehow but underlying the chat, the jokes, the information and the discussion, we as the patients, were experiencing a monstrous intrusion. It felt like it would taint your soul. It troubled me and I imagine it was the same for everyone else in this 'club'. It had a dull deadening weight to it, a kind of impact that suffocated anything that you might regard as a treat. It was overwhelming. We all had a different type of cancer or blood disorder but in common with each other, sat with a straight back in our chairs, taking our medicine.

Whatever baleful shape this treatment formed, there was necessity that came with it. The nursing team delivered exactly what was required and, in playing my part I put my faith in them, just like everyone else in the room, or so I thought.

One person in the room there had the same condition as I - Hodgkin's disease - the only one I have ever met with it. She was about three cycles ahead of me and I was drawn to her as anybody would be. Here was an instant support group sitting in the chair right next to me. I wouldn't even have to shout across the room. Obviously, I was very keen to hear how she was progressing but, before making this clear, she presented me with a huge list of complaints about the treatment we were both having; Loss of hair, loss of taste, infections, sickness and a number of other side effects that I had read about in leaflets. Worse than any of these, though, was her feeling that the treatment was unbearable. She told me it was probably not worth the effort.

After ten minutes I decided that this lady was someone I needed to avoid and so I did. As it happened, our treatment days coincided but, luckily she used to arrive on the ward ahead of me, so I would choose the chair furthest away from her leaving some other poor bugger to put up with that. I had a lot to live for and being positive about this treatment was part of it. My treatment was to progress regardless of her pessimistic viewpoint. I sat next to a man who recently had experienced his home being repossessed by the bank. I wasn't sure whether or not his illness had been the reason for this but he had a positive attitude about recovery and that was the kind of person you needed to be near. In that respect, he had enough wealth to give me a donation and I gladly took it. By the time Kate came to collect me, we had talked about the Premier League, the demise of the corner shop, student loans, the value of Christmas and songs we remembered from our courting days. At the same time we faithfully took our drugs. The only subject not on the list was cancer and we were the better for avoiding it.

On Thursday, I was back at home waiting for the alien to settle in to its 'comfy' place. Obligingly, it left a big enough gap for me to say goodbye to Bill and Stella. They had been so helpful, looking after the little ones and on one occasion when Kate was out, looking after me. As I was waving them off, for some reason, I took a tug at my hair. A great lump of it came out in my hand. It was something I had been dreading happening but when it actually did I wasn't that bothered – I even manged a chuckle. Losing hair is a symbol of cancer that everyone seems to know about, everyone seems able to associate with this inescapable fact. The real truth is, that in comparison to all of the other side-effects, losing hair doesn't count for much.

As I came back in the front door, the phone rang. It had been a busy little thing. It could have been the ward or a friend calling us. I had taken to answering the phone rather than just leaving it long enough for the caller to leave a message. Messages leave you with another job of course. On this occasion, a man asked, 'Is that Pete?'
'Yes' I replied.
'I have found your fiver' he said 'and I'm ringing up like you said on the card.'
It was about the £10 reward! I was shocked that somebody would have actually bothered ringing me.
'Sorry, you're too late. The reward has already been claimed' I calmly responded.

He sounded very disappointed at the news. Later that evening as the alien within started damaging my insides I wished that I had asked the man who rang to come round to the house for his reward - I would have enjoyed seeing his reaction as he entered my bedroom, witnessed the scene, held out his hand, took his ten pounds and left. It would have been worth it!

Chapter 17

Minnie is a great dog. We have been lucky with her. She is a three year old Springer Spaniel which is a breed renowned for being a bit chaotic. She has been brought up and trained in our house so it is hard to understand why she is so sensible, probably the calmest personality in the family. She does need a walk though, at least twice a day. I would recommend a dog to anyone going through chemotherapy treatment. Just when I felt like rolling over and staying in bed, especially in the winter there was always Minnie to walk. She got me out meeting people, provided much needed exercise and was always good company. When I was feeling quite fit, she would pull along to get to the park, but when I was tired out she just took it easy and padded along at the pace I could manage.

The people in the park who walk around during working hours are people that I would never usually meet. I would normally be at work. The lonely, the bereaved and the confused mostly occupy the pathways, along with young mums and the elderly. There are some poorly ones too. I met a mum whose daughter died at eighteen years of meningitis, lots of people who live alone with just their dog for company, a lady who just walks except for the moments in which she stops to drink from a bottle of spirits and a middle aged man looking for his parrot. Looking back now, that group (apart from the parrot seeker) provided a natural support group for me and each other. One lady called Caroline took a particular interest as her husband had recently died of cancer. I liked bumping into her, she always kissed me before saying anything and then had something helpful to say. She told Kate one day about the Wakefield Hospice, who in turn suggested I visit there. Presuming I wouldn't need the help of hospice I discounted the idea until I met Caroline again. Another kiss, then 'I told Kate about the day services at the hospice, did she mention it to you?' It was still a bit of a shock and I replied 'I didn't think I was that ill.'

I reported the conversation back home and within the week Kate had taken Caroline's advice and forced me down to our local hospice. A very friendly and welcoming environment for sure, but I felt stunned as I sat in the chair and waited for one of the team to sit down with us. A lady called Carol soon joined us and explained their role, I was completely unable to speak. The kindness was without question, the environment was bright and lively, the atmosphere was very supportive, but to me a hospice was for those dying of cancer and I couldn't quite believe I was there. The tears were bursting to come out. Keeping my mouth closed somehow kept them at bay. I have since found that keeping your eyes closed stops you talking too. I will have to remember these handy tips for when I return to work. As the visit went on it became clear to me that the name 'hospice' had certainly confused me. Sure enough there was a part of the building which helped cancer patients in the last weeks of their lives, but the day service was very different, I could see and feel that. Even without speaking I was able to arrange an appointment to come down and join in some of the activities. Kate seemed to feel sure it would be a help to us both, all of the faciltiies were open to family and carers too. Kate would be able to gain support too and in truth that was the main reason for going along with it.

The visit co-incided with a present that arrived through the post from my good friends Ian and Bev. They have known me over twenty years and were exactly right in presuming that I wouldn't take well to 'taking it easy' in between treatments. The gift that tumbled out of their parcel included sketch pad, pens, pencils, watercolours and a book on how to get started. This would help me with my first visit to the hospice. The gifts seemed like a little tool bag to help get me across the door and give me something to do when I was there. By the time my hospice appointment came up I had tried out some sketches at home and was able to show the tutor a few bits that were half decent. Her name is Anne and she was very encouraging. She was probably thinking that the sketches belonged to somebody who hadn't drawn anything since leaving school. If so, she didn't give that impression. Anyway, she would have been right.

As I will have mentioned previously the support from friends, family and colleagues had been a massive help. Imagine you are on a long walk, you have both become lost, there is nobody to ask for help or directions and it starts to rain just at the point you realize the new boots are causing a blister after all. You are ten minutes into an awful row about who lost the map and who left the umbrella when on the next bend in the pathway are two people you know well. Waiting under a small gazebo they are making a brew with a bacon sandwich and serving it up on a small table with a dry chair. You can't stop and talk, just long enough to eat the sandwich and drink the tea and then you notice that these two people make no tea or sandwiches for themselves. Refreshed, you set off on the walk again and as you do so they present you with a green transparent bag complete with an ordance survey map, a packet of plasters and a spare umbrella.

In the many forms of help we received, this is how it seemed. The bacon sandwiches and mugs of tea are just a symbol of the many practical things people did for us. Looking after the kids at night time or during appointments, taking them home for tea, inviting the whole family around for a meal, phoning up regularly, lifts from the hospital, a breakfast or coffee outing, knocking at the door with a cooked meal and of course visits from near and far. One friend, Anthony, booked me in for a game of snooker once a month, I went along no matter how I felt. He's a decent player and his kindness ended as soon as the light over the table came on. No mercy! Just what I needed. Some helped with bigger projects like decorating the living room and moving a shed! The list could go on and I could write down all of their names. It could be a little tedious to read though, or even worse I may forget somebody and upset them. Just simply a 'thank you' will do for now, but I have tried to remember everyone at the end of this book. I tried to thank one such friend of mine who came to collect me from hospital following a chemotherapy treatment. I knew what I was trying to say to her, but bungled it. She had to drive twenty miles through rush hour traffic with me as an incoherent passenger before delivering my shaking body to the front door of my house. At which point I said, 'Thanks Jill, if ever you are this ill, I'll repay the favour.

'I'll pass on that if you don't mind' came the instant reply.

Jill got her own back a bit later. As I mentioned earlier my hair had started to fall out and though it wasn't too upsetting, I decided to get it all shaved off. For some reason inexplicable even to myself a touch of vanity has always allowed me to look into a mirror and be pleased with what I see. This time I wasn't sure how I would feel sitting in the barbers staring at myself as what was left of my hair fell to the floor. I was already much lighter than before, a strange grey colour had taken root in my cheeks and my eyebrows and eyelashes were all but invisible. Preferring a less public arena for the shaving I asked Jill if she could carry out the task. She is experienced. She owns two shaggy dogs and has a follicaly challenged husband. She was glad to oblige, there was almost a glint in her eye. Craig her husband was lined up for a shave too, not that he needed it, but she must have thought it would be company for me. The dogs both disappeared.

I had never before had a 'number 1' nor would I like it again. Some people like Craig seem to suit it, but not me. I couldn't quite put my finger on why it looked so awful, nor did I have time to think more about it before Jill presented me with a red hat that she had knitted and a jet black wig that she had bought from a fancy dress shop. I tried the wig on, carefully ensuring the label was at the back and looked into their mirror. I saw Groucho Marx staring back at me. It is 2009, I am stood in a contemporary living room yet there he is looking right back at me, copying my every grimace. Even my colour was right - sepia!

That night we were meeting Jill and Craig at Anne and Andy's house for a meal. I didn't feel too good to be honest, so made the best of my external appearance by leaving the wig at home and wearing a nice new striped grandad shirt that Kate had bought me for my birthday. On the face of it I looked okay though couldn't do much about what was going on inside. As the evening progressed the conversation around me was a blur, I couldn't taste the meal of salmon steak and vegetables thanks to the side effects of the 'chemo' and spent all night trying to stop my arms and legs shaking. It became too much of an effort to try and stop this so I just concentrated on one limb at at time. It was I am sure a very tasty meal and I enjoyed the textures, but trying to socialise even amongst such understanding friends was hard work. I carried on trying and they carried on understanding. When we returned home, I again ventured to the mirror. The striped shirt complimented the bald head in a macabre sort of way. Now I could see why I looked so awful. The person I saw was just like those I had seen on television, those who were occupants of the awful prison camps in the second world war. I felt as if I needed liberating by the Americans. Desperate! The striped shirt would stay at the back of the wardrobe until this particular war was over.

My brother Dave visited us for a few days from his home in Spain. I was very pleased to see him again, but beyond this he could see my distress very easily. Dave helped out in loads of ways, he dismantled my chicken run, tidied up the back yard, cut loads of wood for the winter and did a few jobs around the house too. One day he asked me where we could buy a decent hat for me and off we went to a spot that sells outdoor clothing. We picked out a hat for me that cost £40 and a bandana to wear underneath. He is a bit of a style guru and reckoned this 'Tilly hat' looked well on me. As I tried it on, the situation and circumstances caught up with me and this time I couldn't hold the tears back. Just reflecting on this and how it felt brings them back again. In this busy shop, with the young attendant looking on, he grabbed hold of me tightly and held on to me until I came round. It's a good job we look so alike, anybody looking on must have known we were brothers - I hope so anyway!

I will end this chapter just as I started it, walking the dog. About a week after Dave had returned to Spain I was returning from the park one evening and passed the Cherry Tree, which is our nearest pub. The smokers were all outside looking for some amusement and I was it. The hat was on and keeping the rain off. The bandana underneath was keeping me warm.

'Look at the old git in that hat pretending to Indiana Jones' shouted the chubby one.
His mates laughed with him at me. I crossed the road towards them with Minnie padding along faithfully beside. I removed my hat. 'The reason I wear this hat is that I have cancer and I've lost all my hair'
I walked off, still listening to laughter and scathing remarks, but this time coming from the small circle of smokers and directed at the chubby one who now had nothing to shout about.

Chapter 18

Two months into the treatment a pattern was definitely emerging. For just two or three days out of each fortnight I could be fairly independent then the fortnightly injection would be upon me. Every drug I was given caused an adverse reaction. It was like the song that Walter sang to Liza as each solution to a problem created just another difficulty. Pain in my spine, then some painkillers, each time a bit stronger, then constipation, some more medicine to help with that. Next to join in was the chemotherapy, my little alien and the sickness. Dehydration would set in and result in more weight loss. I began to realise that the next six months would need me to develop a range of coping strategies to patch 'the hole in my bucket'.

I am pleased to say that I have never read a self help book in my life. There are loads of topics that are available. Parenthood, playing with kids, self respect, financial security, diet, exercise, how to think, how to interact, how to be assertive. It is a whole industry and I have never signed up to any of these masterpieces as an apprentice victim. I prefer to spend the £6.99 such a book would cost and the three hours it would take to read with a good friend in the pub. I have decided that the only way to cope with the downside is to recognise the upside too. For example, in amongst all the various problems contained in my fornightly pattern, my night time sweats stopped. First they dropped down from four hours to one then just as my consultant had predicted they packed in after two months of treatment. This made a huge difference in that I could at last get a full night's sleep. It was a real indication that the Hodgkins Lymphoma was being placed in check. I moved back into my bed with Kate. Definitely an upside!

Paradoxically, just as an ordinary day can create problems for me I feel quite able to cope with anything unusual or unpleasant that happens. In 1993 when my first wife left Sam, Rosie and me for the blues singer I remember a day which gave me a confidence and a strength that would help me cope with just about anything that life could throw at me. When she rapidly left the house to live with her new boyfriend she was in too much of a frenzy to take much with her. The whole affair seemed to be such a rush. I had to take some holiday from work, look after Sam and Rosie and hope she would see sense and come back within a few days. We just needed to talk really. Sam was just five and Rosie was four years old. I told them that she had gone to spend a few days with a girlfriend who needed some help. This seemed to help them understand why their mum had suddenly gone from the home. I was right in hoping she would turn up soon, she did, but resolute in her decision to leave. She spent half an hour in the house while the kids were at nursery and gathered a hairdryer, some contact lens solution, a cheque book and a few other things including some wet washing out the machine. Enough to fill a black bin liner. As she was leaving for the second time that week she asked how Sam and Rosie were. I told her they thought she was away for a few days and that is all they knew. I remember she pondered this for a bit then said 'The kids can stay with you, don't worry about that.'

In the madness of the situation I was able to come up with some little bit of clarity that seemed to make an impression perhaps on her, but certainly on me. 'I don't deserve to lose you, so certainly don't deserve to lose the kids too.'

With that she was gone, allowing no time to talk. I didn't know when we would ever see her again. The downside was that Sam and Rosie at such a young age would need to learn the truth. It was a painful task explaining to them what had happened and trying to help them understand that both Mum and Dad had failed to provide the security they needed. I was amazed when they went off to bed in their room, had their usual story at the usual time and quietly fell asleep.

At that time we lived in a house up a long country lane with just one neighbour. There was no electricity from the mains, power was provided from a deisel generator purring away in an outbuilding. Water came from a spring up near the trees and any gas we needed came from portable bottles. A beautiful place, but not so convenient. That is why the rent was cheap. I used to keep the generator running for twelve hours each day. The house was about eight miles inland from Scarborough in the North Yorkshire Moors National Park. You had to drive along a very unpredictable stream for about four hundred yards to reach the house from the main road. Sometimes the stream was shallow, sometimes it would be lapping into the door of the car. As a family unit the house had seemed like a magical place to be. In the first few days of being a single parent it seemed like a cold and barren hole to live in and I dreaded the hours alone once the kids were in bed. I remember that night kneeling down to pray that I would be able to look after them properly. Without the generator on, the place was completely still and the moonlight shone brightly across the landing. For extra light I had placed two candles on the bedroom windowsill. As I finished my prayer this time I noticed that the candles threw off two shadows, each one of me. One was covering Sam and the other covering Rosie as they lay in their beds. I took this as I sign that we would manage.

The next day started at 3am. Rosie awoke and remembered the bad news that I had given her the previous evening. She was sick in her bed and the fuss woke Sam up. More tears. I thought of keeping them off nursery the next day, just to stay at home and play games seemed the sensible option. That's what we did. After lunch Sam asked if he could borrow my walking stick for the nettles and take our little dog out for a walk. It was peaceful and safe there so off he went around the house while I washed up. Five minutes later, I heard the sound of my living room windows breaking. I rushed outside to find Sam braying in the windows with my stick.

62

I picked him up and hugged him tight, he grabbed me back and burst into floods of tears. Rosie meanwhile, drawn to the noise of the glass breaking, found her way to the window, put her hand on the exposed edges and cut three fingers. That was a difficult day, but we got through it and plenty more besides.

I wrote briefly of these events earlier and said it all may surface later on. It has. Somehow it is all to do with coping then and coping now. In reading back over these pages it seems that despite my dislike of them, I have just benefited from my first self help book!

Chapter 19

After my second cycle of treatment I was given a break. It was welcome. It meant the fortnightly pattern would be broken as there would be one month before my next chemotherapy session. The medical team had decided to send me for another PET scan (the one with the toilet facility for radioactive patients.) They wanted to monitor how the chemotherapy was effecting the lymphoma. I knew what to expect this time, so made sure I had a book to occupy myself during the hour in the lead lined room. The book would be no help in the actual scanner and there was point bringing in some music after the last experience. I fancied doing a painting of a London street at my art group, so lay in the scanner imagining what I could include. After an hour in there I had a fair idea about the image I would like to paint. I would include buses, taxis, lamps, shop fronts and the dome of St. Paul's cathedral. I remember that scene well from a school trip I went on while at primary school. Thinking of the painting would occupy most of the hour in the scanner. It would take me weeks to actually complete it.

This time the whole scan session was much less scary because I already knew what was going to happen. Even the hundred yard walk down Radioactive Way to the toilet was less humiliating somehow. Outside the loo there were even more people awaiting their X - rays than last time. In their wait they had little else to do but look curiously at the people using the special toilet. Undaunted, I strode in bravely and this time managed to avail myself of the facility. I didn't even lock the door in my radioactive glow of confidence. Once complete, I met up again with my sentry who was supervising every move and strode again past the rather terrified group of patients. I followed the nurse who walked ten yards ahead of me back to the scanner. This time she had no need to explain why she was being so rude.

The only real anxiety about this event was waiting for the results. To ease the tension during the next few days I started my painting of London in the art group at Wakefield Hospice. I had gained the impression that Dr. Wright and the team in the hospital really wanted to see an improvement, even at this early stage. The wait would last a full week. Meanwhile there were benefits to having a break from the medicine. My hair started to grow back and looked less patchy. I was able to taste food better. I had more energy and didn't have to put up with the injection nor its side effects. There were benefits for the boys too as I could do a lot more with them. I even had a game of football in the park. Joe especially was pleased with this. I thought they were coping very well with the illness and all that it threw at them. Michael, two years older than Joe, seemed certain that I would get better and seemed to take each event in his stride. Any conversation with him seemed very positive. There were no 'what ifs or if onlys' when talking to Michael. He kept his mind and his conversation firmly focused on next April. This he knew would be the time when the planned chemotherapy sessions would be over. By that time he believed I would be back to my usual self. I felt very proud of him for this. His attitude was contagious and made me also believe I would get better. Somehow he seemed to have got it all in perspective. Joe on the other hand found it very hard to look at me without hair, so I took to wearing the bandana all of the time so as not to upset him. I thought it made me look even stranger, but it seemed to do the trick for him.

A week later I was back in Clinic. It was quite a long wait, as usual. We kept pretty calm though as we sat in the corridor. By the time we went into see the doctor a dozen text messages had ganged up on my mobile phone, all from friends and family eager to hear good news. There was no point in replying, we didn't know anything. We held dry hands in his office as the doctor stared at the scan results on his computer. My eyes were also on a nurse who was sat behind us. Did she have a big needle behind her back full of anaesthetic waiting to stab me as the poor prognosis was delivered? Now we had sweaty hands. The doctor swung around in his chair and looked at me over the top of his glasses; 'We have good news there is excellent progress.'

I am still not sure what he meant by this, nor did I hear anything else he had to say. I don't think Kate did either. I remember offering the doctor a handshake and thanking the nurse. We walked out of his office and down the corridor in a daze. It was just like when you are out in the car and get lost. You eventually meet somebody walking along towards you, you stop the car, the window is wound down and you ask the way. It is a great relief when you find out the stranger knows exactly where you need to be going and gives detailed directions. There are thanks offered, the car moves off and you go wrong at the very first turning.

'Weren't you listening?' the conversation goes.
'No. I thought you were.'

The obvious thing to do was to head towards the ward where I get my treatment and talk to Laura or Claire. Though busy they were very pleased to see us. I received my first hug from Laura. They were obviously aware of the scan results and were delighted at the good news. I still didn't understand what the good news was. It felt good, but why? As we were leaving, neither of us with enough sense to ask what was going on, Laura said 'Back to normal now, see you next week for treatment, it's belt and braces from here on in.'

We found our way back to the car and back through the town and onto the motorway. This time I wasn't looking gloomily at industrial estates, but looking at the clouds and the sunshine poking through. Alice Cooper was on the radio singing 'School's out forever.'

During my next appointment on the ward, waiting for my injection to come up from pharmacy. Laura informed me Dr. Wright wanted to see us both in the room with brown leather seats. She must have seen me wince. The last time we were in there we received such bad news. She responded by saying 'You get good news in there too you know.' This time we were able to take the information in. He explained how the PET scan had given a negative result on cancerous activity which was an excellent indicator.

Their aim to get me into remission was partly achieved. As yet no promises were offered and he made sure I was fully aware that the rest of the chemotherapy had to be undertaken. That is what Laura must have meant by 'belt and braces.' I immediately thought, 'only eight to go.' It was to become a countdown and suddenly the Hodgkin's Lymphoma seemed less of an enemy to me than the treatment itself. I never invited the illness in to invade my life but that didn't apply to the enemy. Ironically, I had to allow him in to give me any chance of survival.

Chapter 20

Years ago I spent a day on the Northumberland coast. It must have been a packed day as I remember visiting Bamburgh Castle, Seahouses and Holy Island or Lindisfarne as it is usually called. The beach at Bamburgh was the best I have visited with the imperious castle as its backdrop. Seahouses; well I wouldn't be bothered about returning. Holy Island had a mystique all of its own. Just like all of the other day trippers we had to leave the island as the tide came in or face being marooned to the early hours of the morning. My father in law Bill stood on the safe side of the causeway like King Canute to see if he could gain ten more minutes before we were forced back to the mainland. He only managed five. The local population of the island is now less than a hundred in number and a major source of amusement for them is to witness the visitor's cars underwater as the owner stands on the roof awaiting rescue. The pubs and notice boards on the island have photographs of these events as evidence of the danger.

My main quest was to find out what it was like on the island once all of the tourists have gone and this spectacular tide claims the island back as its own. With this in mind and with my fifth treatment approaching I decided to book a small cottage in the middle of this island's small village. With my optimistic view of a recovery from the disease it would be something that we could look forward to. With my usual reluctance for interaction with communications technology I couldn't face doing this through the internet. (Anybody who has tried to book a flight with Ryan Air will know what I mean.) I rang directory enquiries and asked them for the phone number of the post office at Holy Island. This acquired I rang the Post Office and the phone was answered by the Post Mistress who gladly gave me three or four numbers of people who let out cottages, one of these was her daughter. The first call I made seemed to fit the bill and a week's rental at the beginning of June seemed about sensible. I sent off the deposit with a letter and a cheque and it was booked. If all went well I should be two months out of my treatment but more importantly it gives me an event to focus upon in the belief that this disease would go into remission. A family holiday. A return to some normality and a reason to get better. Either that or lose my deposit.

Chapter 21

This season Joe has been in a football League for the 'under nines'. He plays for Thornes Juniors third team. I had offered to help with the coaching, training and support at the league games for the 08/09 season. I was disappointed not to be able to carry out my promise, I just wasn't well enough to attend football regularly or take part in the training. In September they lost all of their matches except for one, which was a 0 - 0 result. Joe was in goal and gained the 'man of the match' award. I was too poorly to go to that match so Kate went instead. I was shocked when she came back gleaming, full of enthusiasm and going over each save. Prior to this she had shown no interest in football or any sport really. Kate tries to show an interest on account of having two boys, it is a good effort all right but we know she would rather be doing just about anything else. We were once playing a game of cricket on the beach and Michael asked her how many stumps there were in a test match. 'Just the same as we use, three at one end and one at the other,' came her confident reply. I decided to agree. After her trip to the football game, she wrote a big message on the kitchen notice-board.

'Well done Joe, my Man of the match!'

The team never won or drew a game through October or November. As dads and mums on the sideline we were amazed how they could be beaten by ten or eleven goals each week and still turn up for each match as if they were running out at Anfield. They were proving to be an excellent role model for me these kids. In December we scored a goal through a penalty. It must have had a big impact on the scorer, he left the team the next week to join a better team. A free transfer, by the way. Through January the defeats were down to six or seven goals. By February the team, still with only one point, looked as if they may score a goal anytime soon. It came in a 6 - 1 defeat against Ackworth Allstars. With the match already well lost, Joe found himself on the right wing on his bad foot, but he cut inside and fired a left foot shot past the goalie. All the mums and dads jumped in the air. I had a tear in my eye as they came up to say what a good goal it was. In an effort to cover up, I informed them I didn't really see the goal as I had something in my eye. Sure.

Soon there was another turning point. Joe's team played in Hemsworth against a team that were top of the League. They were good. The supporters had their own tent to shelter them from the rain. The team even had six substitutes waiting on the bench while our team could only field six players in total. Hemsworth Terriers as they were known set about annihilating our team and lived up to their name. Joe was in goal again. For the first time we played like a team in the non-stop barrage of our goal. We lost six - nil, but it seemed like a victory somehow and another man of the match award for our little goalie. I had been through a pretty horrible time that week with treatment. It had been exhausting to drive to the match and stand up through the freezing weather. Later when Joe told his mum about the game he was keen to see his name on the notice board again. Next time I walked in the kitchen she had written up in big letters;

Sorry Joe, but this week, Dad's my man of the match.

Joe and I are both Middlesbrough supporters. With relegation threatening to remove them from the Premier League I came downstairs one morning to find Joe writing a very long letter to their manager, Gareth Southgate. His handwriting is all over the place, but you could read it well enough. It suggested which players he should pick for the game against Stoke. He had even helped Mr. Southgate by picking the reserve team too. Joe sent this letter off with a couple of drawings and a word of warning that a victory would be needed as it would be a good birthday present for him.

A week later came a large envelope from Middlesbrough with a couple of match programmes, some information and better than that a personal letter from Gareth Southgate. He thanked Joe for taking the time to select both teams and for his helpful effort. He also enclosed the team sheets they had used in the dressing rooms for both teams. They were only slightly different to the ones Joe had suggested. Finally he wished Joe a Happy Birthday and enclosed a grubby £5 note as a present. Within half an hour Kate had written out a reply and posted it off. I am not sure what she wrote in it, but I guess she expressed delight that amongst everything we were going through he had made Joe so happy. Gareth Southgate became her man of the match. He still is. Both Joe and I were shoved to the sidelines this time. Middlesbrough lost against Stoke - Gareth should have put out the team Joe had suggested to him.

Chapter 22

Returning back to hospital for the next few cycles of treatment was fairly straightforward. I had been bolstered by the news from the PET scan that this treatment was actually working and that was enough to compensate for the after effects of the chemotherapy. I still struggle to describe what this was actually like. It was always worse on Thursdays and Fridays. Kate works on these two days so I was usually on my own. On Wednesday I tried to strike up a relationship with the alien within. At first it was of a friendly nature as he settled into his usual place. Somehow I thought by speaking nicely to him that he would give me an easier time. By Thursday lunchtime we were having a proper row and I would swear loudly at the little bastard. He didn't have to say much, but always got the upper hand. By Saturday our battle would be nearly over. The waters were calmer though he would just send out the odd ripple to remind me he would be back next time. I wondered about my sanity in creating this character, I never got to like him or become fond of him in anyway. He gave me pain I gave him anger, it was almost a fair exchange. He was the enemy, armed with something much stronger than anything I could muster in the way of defence. Whatever protection I could gather seemed inadequate on this battle field, but I was determined to beat him. Endurance was my only real weapon that and the fact that I have always been a resilient little git.

By the end of my third cycle, or six treatments, my resilience was disappearing. The battle looked lost. With my eyes on the main front, my tiny empire was being attacked from behind. These were places that had always been secure before but suddenly became so vulnerable. I began to associate everyday objects and events with things that were going on at the hospital. Even on the good days, these associations would make me physically sick. I found it impossible to drink tea, listen to Radio 2, make toast, eat a sandwich, use hand lotion or read magazines. These were all frequently occurring events on the ward and they became intolerable at home. I had at one point on the ward eaten a chicken sandwich in white bread. Nice sandwiches served with a smile but that was the end of sandwiches for me from then on. I couldn't even think about them without feeling sick, let alone eat one. Sharon served up the drinks and food and she was lovely with it but the sound of that trolley arriving as it rattled along the corridor became a mortal dread to me. I began to fear it more than the trolley that brought my chemotherapy. My sense of taste had all but disappeared by this stage and conversely my sense of smell was better than Clarke Kent's. The taste of chemotherapy invaded anything that tasted bland, which was most things. Strangest of all it took over the taste of water. How did the taste of the drugs get into my tap? It managed to follow me everywhere, it even occupied the tap in my mum's house. It was evident in the bottle of water I bought in the Co-op. I tried different methods of drinking the stuff, warm, cool, cold or freezing but the drugs were still in there however I drunk it. Invisible and ever present. It made me feel sick. By elimination I discovered that it had failed to find its way into sparkling water or ginger ale. These would save me from dehydration over the coming weeks.

There was a particular bottle of handwash in the house, difficult to distinguish which one, but just like the water in the tap, the smell of it invaded every room. In an effort to avoid infection, all bars of soap had been chucked away and been replaced by the press down type that squirts out onto your hand. I even got a waft of this in places I wouldn't expect like in the fridge! It was everywhere. One day when Kate was at work I got all the bottles together and squirted them until I identified the culprit. They all had some part to blame, but there was a Tesco version that was the main sniper. Burping and jipping, I hid it behind the shoe polish kit and a bottle of turps hoping never to see it again. The simplest thing would

74

have been to throw it out but the simple solutions are not easy to come up with. I shouldn't have kept this all to myself because each time Kate polished a pair of shoes the hand wash appeared back on the sink again. I didn't need to go into the bathroom or the toilet to know that - I could smell it. The blooming stuff was out of the cupboard and taking aim at me.

The smells and tastes followed me around until I visited the ward again for the seventh treatment. My friend Chad had taken me this time, he talks a lot about football and this was just the distraction I needed. As I left the lift and opened the double doors to the Dr. Jackson ward I was overwhelmed by the smells of the drugs awaiting me. My breakfast was doing its best to make an appearance and in effort to keep it down I couldn't speak to the cheery team that were there to help me. Chad stayed with me until the first bag of drugs came and then he left - just before I was sick. It is usually the last bag of medicine, the Dicarbazine, that gets me. That was a joy still to come. Today was going to be a long one. Laura and Katherine moved me into a side room with a bed away from all the other patients and the 'shackleton-chair-circle' they sat in. I am sure the feeling of nausea is catching in that situation, so I was better off being isolated. The side room was to have quite a part to play during the rest of my treatment.

Six hours later I was still in in the bed and receiving my last bag through a drip into my arm, when Norman arrived to give me a lift home. He is, I guess quite good looking and this was evidenced by the fact that the nurses spent a lot of time talking to him. While this was going on the shakes that I had experienced at my very first treatment came back. They were not as violent this time but felt strong enough to concern the team about my high temperature and the level of sickness. Norman was a very good visitor to have, as a nurse himself he was able to say the right things and keep me calm. Laura held my hand. Of all the nursing care I received probably this was the most effective. On a ward like this you get touched all the time - you are assisted to the toilet, prodded by needles, moved around and generally made as comfortable as possible but all of these are out of necessity. Holding the hand is not really an essential nursing task but I can confidently say that as a patient undergoing a harrowing time it is the most important piece of protection you can get. This is because it isn't an essential task but simply an act of human kindness. A simple but vital act that can be returned and shared as part of the deal.

Norman was unable to give me a ride home that night as by 5pm I was in an ambulance. The destination being the hospital ward at Pinderfields, the ward where my first treatment had been given. I wanted the ambulance to slow down as each bump in the road shook me to the roots. The journey of just ten miles seemed like it was never going to end. The driver however seemed keen to get me there as soon as possible. The outside temperature that night was around freezing point. As I was wheeled away from the ambulance the night air felt absolutely magical upon my hot skin. It was like a cold pint of Budweiser on a hot summer's day. Perfect! By the time Kate visited me that evening I was in bed with fluids dripping away into my system helping me to recover from the sickness and dehydration. This was a great way to take in water as I couldn't taste it. Could I link one of these machines up to my fridge at home? My temperature was still in the low forties but the shakes had gone. In fact I was quite comfortable in a room all on my own and wondering what the next few hours would bring. Just as I was feeling happier and settling down for the night a volunteer came into my room and offered me a cup of tea and a chicken sandwich made in white bread for my supper!

Later that evening I listened to a radio report about the Israeli attack on the Palestinian population. My busy life prior to this illness had rarely if ever allowed me the luxury of listening to an in depth report on radio 4 late in the evening. As the hour long programme progressed I thought long and hard about the injustice these civilians were receiving and the pain of children who had become injured, killed or lost their parents. Our present government and others posturing in the House of Commons as if they cared suddenly struck me as a cold and callous bunch. Just as I hoped the feelings I have towards a chicken sandwich may remain with me in years to come, I really believed the politicians lack of opposition to Israel was a cowardly act of hypocrisy.

Chapter 23

In what follows I wish to make sure I avoid that 'thought for the day' syndrome that Radio 4 listeners will be aware of. What happens is that the speaker of the day makes reference to something topical to draw you in, it may be the world cup, an earthquake or tsunami, but an interesting event to keep you listening is the most important thing. Then about two thirds of the way through the dialogue Jesus is dragged in to hammer home a point. That's unkind on Jesus, sometimes it is a character from the old testament or a latter day saint. Whatever the cast list, this is the usual format. That is the point at which you will usually change radio channel to something less godly featuring the weather or the sports news. There is no doubt about it, 'thought for the day,' hasn't been the same since the Rabbi Lionel Blue stopped doing it.

Beyond this bit of flippancy keeping a faith and being part of a Catholic community has been a massive support in helping me and Kate through this. At the risk of losing the interest of any reader who has managed to get this far, I can say that even my fragile faith has been something to be proud of. I feel it would be unjustified to ignore it. It has provided a friendship when I have most needed it, especially in hospital. I wrote two prayers in there, one for the morning which helped me face up to any bad news that might be looming and one for the evening before the demons arrived. I read each out quietly to myself and somehow they helped me a lot and still do. Like all Catholics good, bad, or in the middle like me, there is loads of guilt and mine is due to the fact that I believe my faith most when I need it most. In comparison to lots of others I feel quite inadequate sometimes in the consistency of my faith, but it is there. My heightened senses also included a new radar screen which picked up on all the prayers that our community was saying for me.

The school, the kids, the friends in the congregation, the priest and many other people that I hardly knew. I am pleased to write about it and make no apology for it. That's my thought for the day.

Perhaps there is just one more thought. Something I can stand my ground is on Christmas. It means a lot to me and my family but for so many people it's just a chance for time off work, a time to relax and be indulgent. It is sad that there isn't much thought from so many people about what it stands for yet they happily accept its benefits, spend too much money and think about attending midnight mass as the forfeit. That's said and over and done with. This Christmas time though was to be right in the middle of my chemotherapy and was going to be different from any I had experienced before.

I was quite lucky really, the timing of the fortnightly cycle meant that I was feeling quite well for Christmas week and looking forward to the festivities with my family. Sam and Rosie were home from college, so we were complete. The Alien, be assured, didn't take any time off for the holiday season and I was guaranteed a visit for the New Year- I couldn't have it all ways. We went to Church on Christmas Eve and most of Christmas Day was spent with Kate, Sam, Rosie, Michael and Joe. It was while we were opening our presents I underwent the first experience of something that really made me grateful to be alive. On that morning I was very quiet, it was too difficult to speak. I felt joyful, yet very emotional. I had just opened a present Joe and had made for me. It was cardboard box in which he had pasted pictures of Middlesbrough players and painted a picture of a goal being scored on the top of the box. The whole thing could easily have been ripped open with the minimum of effort but for security purposes he had fitted a small padlock and chain to it. It was the best present I could have been given.

79

At that point, still holding my present, I felt my body actually physically lift up to a point about twenty metres above the rest of my family. My stomach lurched as if I was going up in a fast lift. I didn't actually move from the settee otherwise all five of them would have experienced the misfortune of looking up at me through the bottom of my dressing gown. The settee I was sitting on was still on the floor, but I wasn't on it. I just looked down and saw the five of them opening presents and trying to enjoy Christmas without me. *'That's how it could have turned out'* came a voice, it was loud and clear. I shut my eyes to avoid the scene and appreciate the fact that I was holding onto my cardboard box rather than lying inside of one. With that I was back on the settee, nobody had even noticed I had gone missing and I didn't bother telling anybody where I had been. The chaos and celebration of the day carried on but I was brought back down to earth for the second time in the day. I like cooking and I enjoyed cooking the Christmas meal for us all. My mum came round to share it with us. In the hectic preparation I had forgotten one thing – it wasn't until I sat down and started eating it that I rediscovered the problem with my taste. All that effort and all I could taste was the sprouts!

I have another brother, Barry. He gave up on the United Kingdom over thirty years ago and moved to France. Since that time he has enjoyed, or endured, a hand to mouth existence. Whenever I had been to visit him I came away feeling that he is a very lonely soul over there. The whole family was very pleased for him when he met a woman and they married, she was from Indonesia and all at last seemed okay. They had a daughter named Regina and she was about four before their marriage turned sour. Barry's wife was determined not to share this little girl and after a long and complex set of events she took Regina away, In fact she kidnapped the girl and took her back to Indonesia illegally. My brother was distraught of course and faces a long future without his little girl.

One day when Regina is not so little we all hope she will seek him out and rediscover her loving dad. In the meantime he suffers so much due to Regina's absence. Barry came over to spend New Year with us all. This can't have been easy for him - he would be surrounded by my children and they would remind him of the relationship that he had enjoyed with his daughter.

As always we enjoyed each others company but this was disrupted by chemotherapy I received on New Year's Eve. That is where the fun stopped. Barry was shocked at the reaction I suffered to the drugs and did his best to keep me company. Kate and the children had been invited out to a party so Barry stayed with me to see the New Year in. Unfortunately he picked up a virus and a severe cough that day and my fragile immune system meant that we couldn't spend any time together. With just the two of us in the house as the twelve bells struck, he was downstairs having a lonely beer on the settee and I was upstairs vomiting into a bowl.
'Happy New Year' he shouted between his coughs.
'You too Baz,' came my muffled reply as I noticed the strange echo that rebounds from the four sides of a plastic bowl. 'Happy New Year.'

There has been another faith - it is new and somewhat reluctantly engaged upon by myself. It's the support and amazing energy offered by people skilled in alternative and complimentary therapy. I have been a slightly unwilling participant from the very beginning in this peculiar world. Kate is a great advocate however and introduced me to her homeopath who specialises in treating people with cancer. This was lucky for me, Catherine is her name and she asked me to go and see her. I knew from the outset that she had a great deal of understanding about my condition and the effect of the chemotherapy. That was helpful in itself and it felt reassuring to know that somebody was keen to help with the emotional side of the illness in addition to the medical help I received on the ward.

Just as Kate had introduced me to the art group at Wakefield Hospice she introduced me to the idea of Reiki. The therapist for this was called Carol and she gave me one session a week throughout the time I received chemotherapy. I rarely drifted off to sleep during these sessions though I had waking dreams that were very random. Invariably the characters I dreamed up were elderly men from the far east, chinese or asian and lying down with me on the couch or filling up test tubes with steaming liquids. On one particular session the faces of about twenty women all visited me. They were all about my age and all stunning to look at. I never really understood Reiki nor was I interested enough to read up about it. I can say that it definitely relieved the back pain that was caused by the injections I was receiving. The ache would disappear for two or three hours afterwards.

During other sessions I felt a very strong heat on my forehead just as if an electric bar heater had been switched on and hung just over me. It is all to do with energy, I think. The other aspect of this I enjoyed was the five minutes that Carol would spend chatting and discussing any of the side effects that I was suffering. At this point I felt I could reveal all of the aches and pains that came along as 'bit players' alongside the main treatment. Undergoing the chemotherapy needed for Hodgkins Lymphoma is pretty heavy going and throughout I felt reluctant to mention the joint ache, the itching and the veins that felt as if they were burning, the mouth ulcers and the fatigue. As bit players they may only have two or three lines during each performance but they link the plot together and provide a platform for the star attractions who can then perform at their very best.

To assist me in controlling these bit players Carol constantly prepared oils for the bath, mouthwash to help with the ulcers and the lack of taste, creams to help with the burning veins and compact discs to help me relax. These CD's didn't help much as my therapy

82

reluctance syndrome kicked in at this point. (I am sure that anybody, like me, who was conceived in Middlesbrough suffers from this reluctance) so background waterfalls, waves and whale music were more of an irritation and I didn't benefit from them.

In the days when I was too ill to come downstairs I would prefer to open the window and just listen to life going on. From the street I would hear conversations, the postman, dogs barking, Kate talking to a neighbour, kids going to and from school, visitors to the house and Michael playing with Joe in the garden. From the few trees around our house there was a surprising amount of birdsong. I preferred the courting sounds of a pair of blackbirds in our garden to the raucous call of a solitary magpie.

I did listen to the radio a lot, especially the digital stations. BBC Radio 7 was a good companion and distracted me from my discomfort with crime and comedy sessions. The other stations I stumbled on were Planet Rock who paid Alice Cooper to be a DJ and another station that played nothing but birdsong. There was no D.J.' on this station, just sounds of birds, the countryside, buzzing bees, horses neighing and bizarrely an occasional ten seconds of flute music would appear every couple of hours. That felt fine.

Chapter 24

When Ian and Bev sent me the paints I decided that I would send them the first painting I managed to produce. It was quite difficult amongst all these drugs to find myself in a place like a forest or a coastline or somewhere that might provide the inspiration for a painting. Most of the objects that came within my eye line were to do with either the hospital ward or the bedroom. Presuming that Ian and Bev wouldn't like a picture of a shackleton chair or a sick bowl I was pleased to receive a 'get well card' from Marilyn at work. It was a well chosen card and it gave me an idea. It depicted a woodland path deep in growth with sunshine poking through as the steps on the path wound their way up a hill. A nice simple idea and it helped me get started on the first painting I had managed since my 'O' level in 1972.

Usually I bash away at a project until it is finished, often too hastily with the predictable number of errors and mistakes. Flat pack furniture is a good case in point. I usually start the assembly calm enough but soon become frustrated with it, I become sweaty palmed, lose tools and of course that last vital screw that is needed to complete the structure. There is a CD rack in my house held together at the top with a nail and a bit of plumber's tape. I once built a fireplace in the living room which relied entirely on gravity to hold it together - placing a vase of flowers anywhere but dead centre caused it to slant. Painting is different though. I seem to be able to take my time and felt prepared to go into great detail or take a break if something too difficult arose. My London painting of St. Paul's was a good example of this. I had decided to use a bit of hardboard as the canvas and chose the 'dimply' side upon which to paint. This made the detail quite tricky. Gradually the picture appeared pretty much as I had planned a few weeks earlier lying in the scanning machine; buses, taxis, shop fronts, buildings and the dome itself. With a lot of support from my tutor who gave me hints and encouragement I became quite pleased with it. Everyone at the hospice had watched the progress of this painting with interest. The staff and all who visit the hospice are a great support and give loads of encouragement whatever you do. Without fail, anybody who went there believing they were handicapped by an illness, showed a hidden talent in a craft or skill that they had never before taken part in. It is a travesty that we need an illness like cancer to force us into such discovery, without the opportunities that such an illness brings we may never know that there is more to life that sat in a traffic jam on the motorway.

To be truthful the time spent in the art group at the hospice was not my first go at painting since I left school. There had been a couple of large projects in 1993. This of course was the summer in which my first wife left Sam and Rosie and myself at our house near Scarborough. I last mentioned this when she arrived at the house with a bin liner stopping only for a few essentials. Her next visit was more considered. It was arranged in advance and she was to spend some time in the house collecting a lot more of her belongings; clothes, records, paperwork, make up, photographs and all of the other essentials she would need to start a life elsewhere. It was going to be more than I could bear to stay and witness this, so I decided to leave before she arrived. I left her a note, which I have since lost, though I remember it to be as heartfelt as I could possibly make it. There had been mistakes on both sides after all.
  On the bottom of the note I explained I would be in Albert and Ivy's yard working on their horse transporter. They were neighbours who lived out on the main road about a mile away from our isolated home. In the note, I asked her to hoot her car horn or to call in and see me as she passed on her way back to Scarborough town - a town where she was shacking up with her new fella.

At that time everyone in the village would have spotted the old Landrover. I had painted our trusty vehicle in a jungle green colour using a wide paintbrush and then finished it more delicately with two snakes, a giraffe, three monkeys, a tiger and a huge grey elephant. It was finished off with a huge yellow sun painted around the back left corner. We used the Landrover for driving through the stream when the water was high. When the rain fell heavily this was the best solution we could come up with. As a result of seeing the jungle images on our Landrover, Albert and Ivy had asked me to paint a scene on the front of their beloved horse transporter. 'If you ever get time' they asked, 'we would love you to do it.'

With Sam and Rosie at nursery and me needing to be out of the house for my wife's visit I suddenly found the spare time and the urge to get started on their request. The panel they wanted painting was the one that sits above the driver's wheel and in size it was six feet by four feet; so quite a space to fill. I had a photograph to use as the basis for the painting, it was an image of their daughter jumping over a hedge on their white mare. So armed with a set of acrylic paints, this photograph, six different brushes and a Mars Bar, I started the long job ahead of me. I had one eye on the trees and fields that I was sketching onto the panel and the other one on the main road leading from Scarborough to our house. I eventually saw her little car as she drove past Albert's yard on the way to our house. There is no way she could have seen me straddled upon the ladder. Two hours later she drove back - this time thanks to my note, knowing exactly where I was. All she did was to hoot the horn on her car just as I had foolishly asked her to do. She proffered a quick wave, hardly slowing down let alone stopping to talk about all of the serious issues that faced us. That is probably why she didn't stop. My suggestion in the note gave her just the escape route she needed, just a hoot of the car horn and she was gone. I felt devastated and clung to my ladder for twenty minutes unable to sketch another shape or even to apply a splash of colour.

As the rungs of the ladder began to hurt my static feet I started moving again and managed to apply myself to the job at hand. About an hour afterwards Ivy brought me out some sandwiches and expressed her delight at the progress. I was pleased when she eventually left me alone to get on with the job and spent two more hours painting before having to leave and pick up the kids.

I remember two more events from that afternoon. Once I had collected Sam and Rosie from the nursery I started driving home and immediately wondered what I had done with my new glasses. Just at that moment I turned the first bend in the lane and saw my glasses slide across the bonnet of the Landrover. They fell off and I felt a tiny bump as the hefty rear wheel ran over them. I stopped a few yards further on up the road, jumped out of the door. I was optimistic that the £120 I had spent would be spared. In fact my glasses were broken beyond recognition and I knew exactly how they must have felt. I couldn't bring myself to throw the smashed lenses into a nearby bush and carefully lay them to rest in their brand new case before discarding the broken pieces into a dustbin at home. When we arrived back in the house there was the letter laying in the same place that I had left it. She hadn't taken it with her to ponder upon as I had hoped. My careful and thoughtful note had taken me a long time to write in a best effort to make sense of the situation. She had simply read it and penned a two line note at the bottom.

Que Cera, Cera.
Whatever will be will be.

Each weekday for two weeks, I returned to the horsebox and carried on with the picture. It wasn't a paid job, that aspect had never been discussed. For some reason I kept a note of the hours that I had spent working on that rural art therapy. Unbelievably it came to forty six hours. Once the picture was complete Albert and Ivy were delighted. To my eye it didn't stand much of a detailed examination but from the road it looked fine and they were very pleased. Ivy presented me with a bottle. I smiled and thanked them but felt the bottle of cheap Claymore Whisky was a poor do for all of those hours spent perched on that ladder.

As I drove away I felt differently about it. The painting had given me a mission during the time that Sam and Rosie were at nursery. I had been given eleven lunches at a time when it was difficult to think about food and the whisky would taste fine with a good slug of ginger ale in it. There was another unexpected bonus - I would be spending a lot of time over the next ten years driving up and down to Scarborough. I would take Sam and Rosie from Wakefield up to see their mum and deliver them to spend the weekend at her new home in Filey, sometimes I would be picking them up to come home with me. If it was the former I usually felt very glum. It was surprising how often at my lowest ebb I would see that horse tranporter travelling towards me - usually on the 'A' roads in North Yorkshire. Once I spotted it on the M62 heading towards Hull. Albert had looked after the picture, it was shiny and varnished and was the result of the forty six hours that I had spent deep in thought and misery clinging to a wooden ladder.

Chapter 25

The last treatment in the ward had gone badly wrong with the reactions, temperature and ambulance drive. Despite this the planned twelve treatments would continue. The only concession was that they would be administered in a side room. With my eighth session approaching I picked up on some information sent by the Lymphoma Association in one of their regular mail outs to members. This one was about a buddy system that they operated for people like me. I rang and spoke to the charity. It is a small organisation and probably not very well off. For that very reason it was probably much better off. When you make a phone call to this association there is no waiting while you join an electronic queue listening to Greensleeves. There are no buttons to press when you eventually get through and at no point do you need to shout 'Yes' down the telephone. Does anybody like that style of communication? I can't imagine anybody does, but most organisations now insist on this style. I hate it, especially when you clearly state the required response down the line and a robotic voice questions your accuracy. You end up shouting the same answer back this time adding a profanity and sometimes get sent back to the front of the queue or often cut off altogether. The good old days when you were recognised on the phone have long gone. When I used to lose things I would ring the Halifax main national office to report yet another lost item. 'I am ringing to report a lost bank card' I would say limply:
'Is that you Pete?' would come the response.

That's what I call a service and sadly missed. If you ring the Halifax these days you need the mental agility of Einstein. This is not what you get when you ring the Lymphoma Association. It is a real service. A cheerful and lively person who actually sounds pleased to hear from you picks up the phone:

'I am ringing to speak to Anne Wilson please, is she there?'
'I think so, I will just try her office. Who is it please?'
'Pete Vickers'
'Hang on please Pete.' Ten seconds elapse with no music. 'Hello, Pete. She is in, but has just nipped to the loo, can I take your phone number and she will ring you straight back.'
'Sure it is 01924....'
'Sorry to interrupt, I have just seen her passing my window, I will put you through, just a moment....'

That is about the style and that is just what you need when you are about to ring a complete stranger and ask for help coping with your chemotherapy. Ringing the robot just wouldn't work and I would have hung up long before I was able to speak to anybody. It puts you at ease to know that the person you are about to divulge your fears to is a real person who uses the toilet.

The phone call to Anne lasted thirty minutes. Just five of these were talking about the buddy scheme which seemed simple enough to join. She just took some basic details and said that she would try and match me up with somebody of a similar age, possibly with kids and hopefully somebody who had undergone treatment for Hodgkins Lymphoma. The remainder of the conversation was a genuine and definite interest in myself, my illness and how we as a family were coping. It was like talking to a expert friend. When I put the phone down I thought, *if that is how the co-ordinator carries on, what will the buddy be like?*

Just half an hour passed before Anne rang me back to give me the details of my new buddy. She had already spoken to someone called Russell who had agreed to help me. He lives in Nottingham, has an eleven year old child and has been through the treatment for Hodgkins Lymphoma and survived it. It was now down to me. I wrote the information down in my diary. It consisted of his phone

90

number and the best times to ring. I thanked her for the instant response which had frankly taken me by surprise. There was no pressure applied upon me to ring him, just a good luck wish was offered along with a promise to be around on the telephone if anything else was needed. I looked at the telephone number for two days and rang Russell just before I went into hospital for the next session.

I found myself talking to somebody who had been through the ABVD treatment and knew exactly how it felt. The only other person I had spoken to with the same condition was my fellow patient on the day ward. She was so anxious about the side effects that I had chosen not to talk to her about it at all. When Russell spoke to me in such a professional, empathetic and friendly manner I found it hard to find the words I needed. I often feel like that, unable to find the words at the time you need them most. It is usually to do with something remarkable that I see, something that makes me want to say a few words that match the spectacle in front of me. I recently saw six geese flying in formation low across a red sunset and I was completely lost as just how to describe it. I just stated inanely,

'That's nice.'

On this occasion it wasn't what I was seeing, but what I was hearing. Russell sounded very reassuring especially when he said that he had only reached his eighth treatment of twelve before infections and complications took over. Over the twenty minutes we talked I gradually gained the idea that actually I was doing quite well and the call ended with a promise to ring him again. It would be something I would look forward to.

Within half an hour of this conversation Anne from the Association rang to ask how I had got on with my new Buddy. This probable co-incidence also seemed highly efficient. Anne was delighted we had made contact and asked if there was anything else she could help with. I briefly thought of asking her how she would describe six geese flying through a red sunset, then thought better of it. If in reading this book you have helped me raise a few quid for this organisation, you have done a good deed for a lot of people in need of support.

Chapter 26

I was dreading the eighth treatment, probably understandable. The reactions from my last session and all the side effects that came with it were reason enough. The thought of entering the ward was making me feel sick as soon as I rose from bed that morning. As usual the pain in my back from the injections had worn off just in time. I couldn't face the thought of any of the water, the tea or refreshments on the ward, so went down to the Co-Op to buy some ginger ale. I was in a bad mood. As I left the till, there was a lady rattling her tin at the customers. She shouted out her message which I am sure was truncated due to her sloppiness.

'Leukaemia for Children.' Rattle, rattle.

'Don't you think the poor little buggers have got enough trouble without that as well!' I rattled back.

Poor woman, bad Pete. I set off home slowly working my way back up the hill to prepare for my hospital visit. My mobility was at times very poor, mostly due to the effects of the injection. It took me ages to get anywhere at these times. I must have looked a sorry sight to the local shopkeepers. It felt important to keep moving especially at these times. Leaving the house, thinking of tea, buying some food and returning were all important jobs. It was also surprising how much support I received from the newsagent, the butchers, the DIY shop, the delicatessen and the greengrocer. These kind folk would never fail to ask how I was and offer encouragement. That meant a lot to me. Others didn't really bother and just did what shopkeepers do; take your money and look at the next customer.

I once owned a fancy dress shop in Scarborough during the late eighties with my first wife. I liked to think we made a big effort with the customers. The only trouble was that there were very few customers. At Christmas, New Year and Halloween we were rushed off our feet. The rest of the year was spent window dressing by changing the costumes on the mannequins and waiting for someone to walk in. Sometimes I was so bored that I would actually put on a costume myself and stand in the window very still until someone walked past. One day a group of infants were out with their teachers and stopped to look in the window. Anne Boleyn and Henry the Eighth were on show that day and dressed as a mad axe man I took great delight in swinging my plastic axe into the Anne Boleyn's neck. The kids hooted with delight as their carers tried to usher them away. As I resumed my still life pose I wondered what the kids would say to their parents that evening.

Soon after that my friends Ian and Bev came to stay for a couple of days. It had been very quiet in the shop all weekend. The bell on the door had only rung twice and total sales in my 'Dimplex C' accounting book totalled thirty five pence; the result of sale to a small child who wanted a false moustache. The other customer looked around, tried on three costumes and left without hiring anything. That evening as were preparing a meal with our friends a phone call came through from the Queen's Hotel at 6pm. It was from a secretary responsible for organising the Conservative Party conference being held at the Scarborough Spa Centre.

'We are holding a Ghost and Ghouls party tonight and looking for someone who can get forty or fifty costumes into the hotel reception by 7pm.'

Without any hesitation I agreed. Within ten minutes I had removed the roof from my Citroen 2CV and forced Ian into helping me load in the costumes, a fold up table and two clothes racks. With just thirty minutes left that job was complete. I found a cash box and a receipt book and we were ready to go. There was just enough time for us both to put on a costume and drive the short distance to the hotel. Dressed as two muscle bound Dark Sci-Fi Lords we arrived in the reception of the hotel and set up our stall. It was John Major's Conservative party at that time.

For those who can remember the television programme 'Spitting Image' it was quite an experience meeting these politicians as they thumbed through the costumes. The resemblance to those hideous puppets was uncanny. Had the Spitting Image team gone far enough in their portrayal was my question? We were only in the hotel reception an hour before all forty two costumes had been taken at ten pounds a throw. Four hundred and twenty pounds, all in cash was sat in my tin box. They asked for receipts, fair enough at the time. Knowing what we know now it was probably all claimed back from me, Ian and all the rest of us tax payers. Ian and I stayed just long enough to take off our masks and have a pint. We even saw some of the costumed politicians and partners come down the grand stairs from their rooms dressed as witches, wizards, fairies, goblins and dwarves. I don't remember seeing John Major or Edwina Curry that night. Perhaps they were busy doing something else! I do remember thinking the costumes markedly improved the appearance of his cabinet office and the vaguely familiar backbenchers. That was a great night, Ian and I had withstood the alarming pace for two hours and had reward for it. Total takings for the weekend, four hundred and twenty pounds and thirty five pence.

As I trudge up the hill now though, pondering my encounter with the Leukaemia lady in the Co-op, my pace is much slower and more painful. Kate had worked some magic and had managed to get us a temporary disabled parking badge which would help when trying to park up near the hospital. On the first day that we had this badge we swung into the car park and looked for the allocated spaces. There was the usual battle for spaces going on and we were narrowly beaten to the last space by a beaten up blue Citroen Saxo. Kate decided to drop me off near the entrance and drive off somewhere else. As I limped past the Saxo I noticed the driver remained seated with a guilty look on her face and showed no parking badge. I was disappointed that the first time I was entitled to use this facility was ruined by this lady and wandered up to her window. She wound it down.

'Excuse me, but have you a badge which allows you to park here?' I enquired politely.
'Yes, but it is at home, she replied curtly.'
'In that case, maybe I should have been allowed to park here instead of you.'
'Mind your own business!' she answered back with a raised voice.
'It is my business if I am entitled to park here and you are not,' came my pompous response.
'I am here on hospital business, so back off.'
'Have you any identity?' I asked, digging a hole for myself, but also quite enjoying the moment.

With that she flashed a West Yorkshire Police badge at me adorned with her photograph. 'I've told you to mind your own business, now bugger off!' She wound up her window and bugger off I did.

An hour later I was lying on a bed in my side room with the first bag of drugs dripping into a vein in my left hand. While waiting for my mate Alan to arrive I began to think that the driver of the blue Saxo, even if on Police business, had no right to park there or talk to me like that. This was reinforced by the opinion of Alan who soon arrived and heard the tale. It was an excellent distraction from the drugs as we discussed the likely contents of a complaint letter to the police. It was a good 'hoot' and helped pass the time.

That subject soon changed to another and another. Three hours passed by which time we had discussed motorbikes, holiday destinations, jobs, wives and children. By that time Alan had also made quite an impression on the nurses by recounting one of my previous visits to a casualty department in Scarborough and challenging them not to think of a red bus. Rachel in particular couldn't think of anything else all afternoon.

Alan's job was to stay until Kate arrived. He must have been well briefed by her. When it was time for the dreaded Dacarbazine to go in, he was still there. I don't remember too much about that. I know he was determined to help me manage the shakes and nausea just as Kate would have described to him. He sat by the edge of my bed as those effects set in. He didn't hold my hand or anything like that and decided to adopt the role model approach. Alan slowly started breathing in a noisy and noticeable fashion so by his example I could repeat his pulmonary action. He took it very seriously and in normal circumstances I would have had a good laugh. Instead, whatever sedative I had taken just took me off somewhere else and that place was a maternity ward. I was looking down at the scene from somewhere near the ceiling. There I was lying in bed, heavily pregnant and awaiting the imminent birth of a child. Alan took the shape of a nervous and expectant husband breathing alongside me just as he had been shown at the new Dad's class. Thankfully that was not the case, this was only cancer. The image of my pregnant self was pure fiction fashioned by the drug. The one inescapable fact truth was lovely Alan. Whenever I came round or started to shake, there he was, right next to me, breathing purposefully. He only stopped when Kate arrived. With friends like that who needs Lymphoma?

The journey home was a difficult and precarious one and I was pleased to get into bed. I enjoyed the two or three hours of rest before the inevitable happened. During that respite I had penned out a letter to the West Yorkshire Police Complaints Department. I used some of the ideas Alan and I had discussed ten hours earlier about my encounter with the driver of the blue Citroen Saxo. Kate wouldn't let me send it, but in good style I toned the letter down to avoid the personal remarks about her wrinkled appearance and her foul manner and just stuck to the facts. It wasn't as amusing anymore, but off it went in the post.

The Leukaemia lady, the local shopkeepers, the axe man, the conservatives, the wrinkled policewoman, Alan's breathing and Kate of course had all contributed in helping me through another session. One that I had been dreading. Now just four to go.

'You are two thirds of the way there' said Michael that evening, who kept a tally on my treatment. He is very good at Maths. I looked back at the long road already travelled. There was no doubt about it, that road looked much shorter than the one that still lay ahead.

Chapter 27

My sister Louise doesn't live far from me. The only brother or sister who doesn't. With Pauline in Cornwall, David in Spain and Barry in France I was beginning to regret the fact that families don't stay close enough anymore. It was quite a long journey to hospital especially in the heavy traffic. My local hospital at Pinderfields had no room for me when I was first diagnosed. That is why I ended up in Pontefract at the medical admissions ward. I really felt concerned about that place and the pressure that the staff were working under. Once I had been diagnosed and met the medical and nursing team on the Dr. Jackson ward I felt very happy to continue my treatment there despite the journey. It took about forty minutes which I usually spent quietly sat next to whoever had volunteered to take me along and contemplated the day ahead. Somehow this rota of drivers and companions all fitted into place, allowing Kate to arrive at work on time, the kids were never late for school and it gave me cheery company. I didn't really think about this at the time, but it must have taken a lot of organising and Kate was behind it all. On the next occasion it was Louise who gave me a lift into the hospital.

When she had dropped me off I tread my now familiar journey to the Dr. Jackson ward. Through the busy car park and up to the main entrance, past the pyjama clad smokers, my usual acknowledgment to the volunteer who welcomed all, past the phone box, into the stairwell, up two flights of stairs and through a double set of doors. That is when the smell of the drugs, the hand gel and the tea trolley hit me harder than usual. As I moved to the nurses station my spine sent a chill around my whole body and my stomach felt like someone was using it as a trampoline. Laura and Catherine were already prepared. All ready and waiting was the side room again. It was nice and cool in there and far away from the main room where all the other regulars received their blood transfusions and chemotherapy. It was a massive relief and reduced my anxiety levels greatly.

As a medical team they had been discussing the fact that the treatment was not going smoothly. In an effort to ensure that I wasn't to be carted away in an ambulance again they had decided to give me a dose of Pethadine just before the final bag of chemotherapy was administered. It was an unusual strategy apparently. I have very little knowledge of drugs, their uses and side effects. I could remember this one though. It was the drug that Kate had been given when she was giving birth to Michael. I was never quite sure what the benefit of it was, perhaps it was pain relief, maybe it had helped relax her for that final push at the end of a difficult labour. It certainly loosened her tongue. As the labour had worn on the nursing team were expecting to carry out a caesarean at the advice of a lady doctor. I remember the doctor hanging about by the door waiting to take Kate to the operating theatre. As the Pethadine took effect Kate spotted the doctor lurking at the back of the room and shouted

'Don't think I can't see you. I can see you, standing right there sharpening your knives!'

I didn't undergo such an aggressive reaction to the Pethadine. It is difficult to remember exactly what went on, but when the shakes started I was able to control them very well. Kate was there helping me to relax and breath slowly. She held my hand and somebody else was gently stroking my forehead. Previously I had been unable to prevent the shakes and unable to stop their acceleration. This time it was much more controlled and didn't spiral out of control. It didn't stop me being sick, nor did it stop me talking in a random fashion about anything that was on my mind at the time. As I came around and staggered to my feet preparing for the journey home I apparently made comments about Kate's breasts which embarrassed everybody in earshot, especially Kate. It is a great drug that Pethadine.

As I left the ward I heard a number of comments from those around me.

'Only three to go. It is all downhill from here, you've broken the back of this, the light is at the end of the tunnel, just three more.'

The thought of just one more of these treatments was enough to make me refuse to go back again, let alone three. It had come down to this, a countdown. To anybody else it was just three more treatments. By the time I had journeyed home and set about my battle with the effects of this medicine I felt absolutely sure that I had just endured my last treatment. I couldn't stand anymore and felt the remaining sessions would have to be dispensed with. The journey home was a fragile and delicate event and usually carried out by Kate. Sometimes her work and the child care arrangements that we needed wouldn't allow her this time and once again our friends would step in. My mate Alan, the breather, did this for me a couple of times. On one of these occasions I felt really poorly. He drove the ten miles so slowly and carefully, avoiding the bumps and humps, the braking and the accelerating. It was as kind a journey as possible. When I arrived home I had to be helped up to bed to wait for my alien.

The alien visited me that evening for the ninth time. I set myself for the usual three days with this horrid little character. Saturday seemed like a long time away, a long and arduous battle until he would leave me alone. At some point on the Thursday I rang my buddy Russell from my bed. I am not sure I was very coherent. Whatever I managed to say prompted this reaction,

'Listen, Pete. If I could only say the magic word to make all this go away for you I would, but I can't. All I can say is that I have been there, I know exactly how it feels, I know exactly what you are going through. It will ease off soon, believe me.'

I wasn't able to respond properly and I soon said goodbye. I lay on my bed stiffly with every muscle tense and fighting the pain. The joy of speaking briefly to somebody who knew what this felt like was overwhelming. The tears soon came. I cried loudly and alone in this empty house partly in absolute despair and partly in an acceptance of the situation. When this crying stopped I realised somehow that I would be able to face the next treatment. Somewhere in the last ten minutes the magic word had been uttered and it had worked, I just didn't know what it was or who had said it. The phone rang and I could reach it from my bed. It would be very unusual for Russell to ring me back, that wasn't how it worked. A male voice was on the line

'Mr. Vickers?'
'It is.'
'Sergeant Jackson here, as the serving officer for the locality concerned I have been allocated your letter of complaint. We have run a trace on the Citroen Saxo and nobody in the police force owns such a vehicle, I am glad to say. We are aware of the owner and will be visiting the aforesaid registered keeper this week.'
I felt too ill too reply at any length and just wondered if the police speak like that when they get home to the wife and kids.

'Would you care at this point to give me a more detailed description of the lady you encountered at this incident? It will be important to me.'

'Not much to say really, she was sat in the car, a pageboy hairstyle and she was incredibly wrinkled,' - it was all I could contribute.

With that Sergeant Jackson thanked me, asked me to write as much down about the incident as I could remember and promised to get back to me. Another five minutes of this awful day had passed.

I was very pleased to see Kate when she came home from work that day even though most of her evening was spent with Michael and Joe. Once they were settled and off to sleep, Kate diverted her attention to me. It wasn't going well and I could tell she was worried. By 10pm my temperature was well over forty degrees. With this condition I am to ring the specialist oncology ward in the local hospital whenever my temperature goes beyond 37.5. The risk of infection is high and if it sets in then antibiotics are needed to fight the infection and avoid possible complications. It is not a particularly great prospect when you are feeling so ill from the chemotherapy to find that you must journey into hospital. The rising temperature left no choice and the phone call was made. I could hear Kate on the phone. She began calmly then her voice changed in its urgency. I could hear her pleading with the nurse on the other end of the phone. The call ended and Kate came up to the bedroom to present me with the situation. She was very upset. There were no beds available in the specialist ward. She had been told that I must come into hospital and that my point of entry would be Accident and Emergency.

It was hard to believe that I would have to go and sit in there on a Thursday night alongside anybody who had been injured in a pub or the street. The prospect was too hard to contemplate, the nausea was extreme as was the fever I was experiencing. I was unable to keep down even a sip of water or any of the tablets that may help me control the temperature. We made a decision not to go. I was prepared to take my chances and by 11pm Kate had me covered in wet flannels, towels and had dug out an electric fan from

103

somewhere in the cellar. Lying underneath all these cold flannels and feeling the icy blast of cold air I could do nothing but admire Kate and the way she was coping with this situation.

There are some, perhaps many, who regard her as a bit of a worrier. Friends and family would admit to this, certainly my consultant thought the same. Here she was carrying out such a high level of care without any training, just instinct. Eventually, I settled down cooler, calmer and relieved. By now it was light and just a short while later the kids got up to get ready for school.

Chapter 28

By Monday I was looking forward to a few days of being quite well. The various side effects though irritating had little impact in comparison to three days I had just experienced. Walking was very difficult for one thing. That wasn't to be a problem as I sat in the Hospice and finished my picture of St. Paul's Cathedral. I am not sure how many hours it had taken me. I didn't count them this time. It has faults for sure, but I felt quite proud of myself when I took it into a picture framers to complete the job. I already had an idea for my next project. Kingfishers. I have only ever seen two, one flying above a small stream near a French campsite and the other flying along the canal at Huddersfield University. I feel quite fascinated by them and presume I am not alone in admiring these bright and feisty little birds.

Also this week I started clearing out our front room to be ready in time for my mate, Paul. He is a decorator in Northallerton and was coming to help me paint the room at the weekend. It was a big job clearing everything out, moving furniture to the centre of the room, covering everything. By Saturday morning I had finished just in time. All the wood surfaces were sanded down and the undercoating was finished. My legs and arms felt limp and frail by the time he arrived. Paul spent the full day putting on the emulsion and glossing woodwork, most of the work he did alone, the effort of getting ready for him had worn me out. It was a brilliant piece of help, especially from somebody who had just spent his whole working week painting living rooms. Here is another friend whom I have known for twenty five years. We have played in the same football team, lived in the same house, bought a caravan to live in and even shared a relatively unsuccessful fancy dress business together. Paul came to visit me regularly throughout these months and another chapter of our friendship has emerged.

When I first met him he was renting a room in the same house that I moved into. I remember thinking how helpful he was when he persuaded me to swap rooms with him so I ended up with the bigger room. Plenty of space for my golf clubs and visitors. I found out a couple of months later that it had cost me £3 a week by doing that, money that he saved. He is as most people would describe ' a likeable rogue'. I think he is too, but there is quite a lot more to him than that. When we were swapping rooms I remember looking at his books. He was a book club buff. There was literature on the occult, nature's forces, space, wildlife, first aid and lots on natural phenomena. He was quite successful with the ladies too and far outshone any of my blundering efforts. I remember being in the Fleece in Northallerton with him one night when an attractive girl approached us.

'Excuse me. Have you the time?' She enquired of him

'If you have the incrincat... incratination... inclention... sod it, it's 8.30!' He stammered. Paul then went onto describe himself to me as someone with a 'speech impigament' which seemed to emphasise the point.

More recently he was stood eating an ice cream watching a ladies Race for Life event. It was a hot day and one of the girls shouted 'Give us a lick,' as she bounced by.

'When I have finished my ice-cream, he replied cockily.

He's not too bad with words of only one syllable. I therefore presumed he was more of a reader than a talker. There was an event which proved this to me, but it wasn't quite the literature I had in mind. We were having a few days in the South West Scottish Highlands, it was getting late when we spotted a sign by a gate.

Fishing boat. Rods, lines and bait included. Enquire at farm on the left.

This seemed like an adventure, especially with our recent pub visit bolstering our confidence. So we enquired at the farm on the left. The farmer must have quickly recognised the fact that we were neither boatsman or fishermen, but the twenty pound note was enough of a rod, line and bait to him. He quickly had us into his Landrover and down to the jetty that was jutting out into this tidal loch. He persuaded us into the boat as the light faded and the wind suddenly became more lively.

We were never to see him again, his parting words were I believe something of this nature (try to read it as if you were listening to Kenny Dalglish.) 'The wind's getting up and the light is going, keep away from the weed, if the engine gets snarled lift it to clean it. If things get bad use the oars. Here is a two way radio. Keep it open, I will be listening out for you.'

In truth this recollection of advice is mainly conjecture. It was at the time, very difficult to understand him in part due to his heavy Scottish accent, our thick English ear, the eight pints of McKewans, a heavy wind and the lapping of the waves on the side of the boat. Imagine our confusion as he started up the engine and then pointed us towards Alaska. Not only were we trying to steer the tiny boat as the waves crashed over the front bit, we were trying to look at least semi competent in fitting bits of dead mackerel to a huge hook.

Despite the gale, the engine soon shifted the boat away from his glare and away from our twenty pound note. The last we saw of him was a dim image of his Land Rover driving back to the farm. Within ten minutes the engine began to throb a little, then gave up the ghost. As the boat slowed we were indeed surrounded by thick black gunge. We had a least the presence of mind to turn any switches off and lift the engine out of the water in order to clear its little propeller shafts from thick, slick and lively Scottish seaweed. With this tricky act completed we put the engine back in the water and it even started up again. That was a mistake, we should have used the oars. This time the engine started to smoke in protest and the cleaning operation was to be repeated. I cleaned away the seaweed as Paul rowed us away from trouble to clearer water. This time the engine didn't start. We bobbed away feeling much less secure relying entirely on skills with the oar which in itself was only based upon the ten minutes of experience we had just gained.

All of this was enough to make us forget about the fishing itself. Somehow we were determined to at least get the bait in the water. We lowered the anchor on its rope only to find that the rope wasn't long enough to reach the bottom. Our fishing began with every chance of failure. The only catch was landed even before the badly frayed piece of mackerel actually hit the water. A seagull dived down and caught it in midair. It was shrieking and yelling as we reeled it in. Blimey, they are big birds and bloody ferocious! Paul had to help me release the monster. There is believe me no quicker way to sober up than carrying out this activity. With a sigh of relief and significantly scratched we sat back as the huge billed bird flew away. I noticed four things in the water, there were two seals and one of them was definitely smiling. The other two objects were our oars, some twenty yards away from the boat.

Without oars or a motor our interest in any more fishing completely disappeared now only aware of the broadside of waves to our boat, another smiling seal and the fact that we were drifting. Soon a very sharp range of rocks came into view. As the wind grew stronger they became nearer. It was very difficult to decide what to do. At that point Paul had an idea and it was then that I discovered exactly what his reading material had been:

'The two way radio' he exclaimed and grabbed it from the water that was gathering in the bottom of the boat. He pressed the button and shouted 'Mayfair, Mayfair!'

Just before the radio went dead we heard a cackle of laughter from the farmer sat in a warm chair somewhere to the east.

Chapter 29

My next treatment was looming confirmed by the fact that I was back at Dr. Jackson ward for my fortnightly injections. The ones that would boost my white blood cells to the point where I could benefit from the chemotherapy. Everybody was telling me 'Just three more to go.' As I reported to the nursing station for this now routine procedure I asked them a question. It related to the lady with Hodgkins disease, the one who was finding the side effects difficult to cope with and the lady I was trying to avoid. I hadn't bumped into her lately and we usually met on Wednesdays. I just asked how she was getting on. The two nurses on duty at reception glanced at each other and their eyes dropped away from my enquiring gaze.

'She didn't make it' replied the sister on duty. 'Not to do with the Hodgkins disease - there were complications.'

My immediate reaction was to reprehend myself for deciding not to talk to her very often. She had been the only other person I knew with the same condition as me after all. Later as I sat at home I became very upset. It is difficult to explain exactly why. I only had to think of our five or six meetings and the conversations I had shared with her husband and a blanket of sadness descended on me. Another sink was needed to accommodate my tears. On reflection it was a mixture of things. Here was a real person that I had known, a lady that I had spoke to and shaken hands with. Someone with the same condition as me. Somebody who was having the same medicine and having a hard time as a result. A person with a caring family and a caring husband that I had come to know quite well. I had read quite a lot about the condition and the likely survival rates which appeared to be good. The news of her death made all these statistics seem hollow and irrelevant.

It wasn't the Hodgkins that killed her I was informed. 'complications' had been the culprit. Whatever that actually meant I was left to discuss with myself. Had it been to do with another condition that I didn't know about, perhaps a heart problem? Did she have something else that complicated the treatment and reduced its effectiveness? Was it a high temperature and a subsequent infection that had taken her? These were a few of the many questions that I asked myself. Why I wondered hadn't the nurses explained it to me. None of my business was the probable answer. Whatever the circumstances the news was a shock and lodged itself under my skin like a splinter. I couldn't manage to get it out so had to make a conscious effort not to think about her. When this failed I thought of her not as a separate person undergoing similar problems, I began to think of her now in a collective term such as 'us' and 'we.' The underlying fear of course being my bad reaction to the medicine, the high temperatures and likely 'complications.'

Some of this may be irrational and probably is, especially to any nurse or specialist reading this. I haven't had the night sweats for over two months now, but a dream I had changed all that. The scene was the Dr. Jackson ward and just as some dreams go it was all very realistic. One of my peer group on the ward called Eric was arriving for his fortnightly session. He reported to the nursing station as usual to see where they wanted him for the day. He then casually enquired;

Where's Pete, I haven't seen him for a bit?'
'He didn't make it,' they replied, 'there were complications.'
I woke up sweating that night and what a relief it was to realise that it was just a dream.

'Are you okay?' Kate asked sleepily.
'Sure am, just make sure Eric knows I'm still here.'

111

Chapter 30

With gathering fears about my reactions to the chemotherapy and the likely impact of my remaining sessions Kate had called in the troops. On this occasion it was my brother Dave from Spain. He had been over before and helped with the kids, the jobs around the house and helped me buy my hat. This was his first visit to the oncology ward and the first time he was to meet the nursing team. I felt very sorry for him as he sat in my allocated side room awaiting the chemo trolley. He looked to be in a state of shock. We are very similar in many ways, though I am better looking. He is ten years younger than me and we did a lot together when he was little. I had coached his football team in the Youth Club and taught him how to play golf. When I left home at eighteen years old I remember wishing he could come along with me.

Dave sat at the end of the bed, nervously balancing on the edge of a plastic chair doing his very best to cheer me along. I knew exactly how he was feeling. The first time I saw those medicines being wheeled in confirmed that I definitely had a cancer. Until then the fact had escaped me somehow. He was now undergoing a similar realisation. For me five months had passed since that time and the progress this medicine had made on my lymphoma had been impressive. The treatment had definitely become an essential enemy battering away at the boundaries to my tiny empire. The actual condition, the Hodgkins Lyphoma had been the reason for the start of this war. As in most wars the reason for its commencement seemed to be of less importance than the impact of the fighting carried out within its duration.

I could tell Dave was undergoing the same initial feelings of shock that I had experienced. He saw the ward, smelled the drugs and felt the gravity of the situation. Unusually, there was a television blabbing away, set high on the wall, perched on a swinging arm. I always admired those swinging arms and the brackets that adhered them to the wall. They seemed very solid and I admired the skills of the worker who must have fixed these televisions onto the walls in each of the side rooms. Not easy on a studded wall. We had a very heavy basket ball net with a similar bracket at home. I had never managed to fix it properly even though it was a solid wall. It looked fine until somebody threw a basketball at it. When that happened the bracket, a piece of stone and some pointing fell to the ground as the bracket came loose. We still have the net lying around in the garden waiting for somone more adept than I to visit our house and volunteer to fit the bracket to the wall properly.

This and many other meaningless thoughts and encounters flitted through my mind as we both awaited the drugs trolley, occasionally turning our head to the breakfast television programme hosted by Philip Schofield who was interviewing somebody called Paris Hilton. In any other situation we would chat away about this or that with no difficulty - the thought of what lay ahead effected our usually comfortable relationship.

'Have you seen that film of her on the internet?,' Dave enquired, trying to lighten the atmosphere.

I had no idea what he was talking about as we don't have the internet. When we do use the world wide web at our local library it is usually for rail tickets or to learn how to build a compost toilet. Paris Hilton was not on our radar. Dave proceeded to tell me a little about this apparently famous film and the impact it had had on lonely or even not so lonely males across the world. It was interesting. There was little time to find out more before my first bag of drugs arrived.

113

Laura and Rachael were looking after me again. As a patient on the ward I recognised that each of the nurses had a special skill, some more experienced than others. It must be a very difficult job, especially when recognising the intimate level of care required to help us patients through this procedure. I thought again about the lady who had died recently. How was it for the nurses when a patient they had nursed and cared for so well didn't pull through? I had no idea about the system they had allocated to me as a patient. I just knew there was one. Over the past months I had received fantastic treatment from each of the team. I felt convinced I would never be able to forget what they had all done for me.

I gained the comforting feeling that one nurse in particular had been allocated my case, probably as the 'key worker.' It was Laura. I had first met her when she sat in the room with brown leather seats as Dr. Wright gave Kate and I the news about my diagnosis. Laura had been a prominent character in my programme ever since. Dr. Wright never really gave much away beyond the clinical information we needed which was fine for me. On one occasion in clinic we were discussing my reaction to the medicine. I had confessed that I felt the remaining treatments would be too much for me. We went on to discuss the various strategies that were being set up to help me. I then complimented the nursing team for all their efforts hoping he would, in turn, feed this information back to them. As usual it was all rather formal. He then said 'Laura has taken it on as a personal mission to get you through this.'

On the outside I tried to remain calm and just expressed a slight smile in response to this information. On the inside I felt great. Laura and I had spoken often over the past months. She had met most of my family, joked with many of my friends, listened to my worries, knew all about my work and had the measure of me and my mischief. It occurred to me that she understood all the reasons in my life that made me want to get better and was doing her best

114

to make sure I did. Of all the information Dr. Wright imparted to me during our appointments this had been the most valuable by a country mile. It had nothing to do with the clinical aspects of my condition, nothing to do with survival rates, the drugs or dealing with the resulting side effects. Just a plain and simple message about the impact one human being was having upon another.

With this assurance I settled for the day ahead. Dave was doing his best to keep me company, Laura and Rachel were looking after me and Kate was arriving later in the day to see me through the worst part of the process, the fourth bag - the dreaded Dacarbazine. I always felt much better when Kate arrived. I couldn't control the sickness but this was of less a concern than the shakes that the Dacarbazine brought on. I felt sure they would come back to pester me again. This was to be a long day. The idea of giving me Pethadine certainly had helped previously so this was to be continued as part of my programme. As the effects of this particular drug took over a problem emerged. The Dacarbazine hadn't arrived. A problem at the laboratory where it was processed had prevented its arrival and it had been placed on a special order as a priority. It took nearly two hours to arrive. This was a shame as everybody had worked so hard to ensure I was in the right state of mind to have the least stress as possible. I was aware of this delay through my drug enhanced daze and accepted the fact that not everything could always go to plan.

By the time the Dacarbazine did arrive I was still very sleepy and it was administered to me as usual. Just as was normally the case, I felt my legs begin to shake. Before long my whole body would be bouncing around - or so I thought. Both of my hands were being held and I heard Kate's voice which was assisting me calmly through my reaction. Holding onto me like this, she could easily tell when I was starting to shake. Whenever this happened I heard her encouraging me to relax, to breathe calmly and to control my body.

In addition to both of her hands there was another on my forehead. A few hours afterwards Kate told me that I had asked her a strange question during all of this activity:

'How many hands have you got, Kate?'
'Just two' came the answer.
Who's at the end of the third then?' I continued.
'It's Laura,' Kate replied.

No private health scheme could have looked after me any better. I am confident of that.

Dave meanwhile was still sitting on his plastic chair at the end of the bed marvelling at the effort both my nurse and my wife were applying in an effort to keep me stable. He later told me of his admiration for them both. He also told me of something else that had occurred during these moments. It had gone something like this - all thanks to Philip Schofield and that television still hanging securely on the wall

'Kate,' I had asked. 'Where's Paris?'
'In France, Pete.'
'No, Paris Hilton is she here?'
'She's here Pete - holding onto your other hand.'
'Good, I'm pleased.'

At the end of the bed, Dave was squirming in his seat wondering if I was going to elaborate on our brief conversation earlier. He was ready to intervene by doing something drastic like pretending to faint. He didn't have to, I was happy and silent in the knowledge that Laura, Kate and Paris Hilton were all there. Each one of them holding onto a different bit of my anatomy.

Dave spent three more days with us at home helping Kate and the children through the time when I felt so ill. I told him about my unwanted visitor 'the alien' and he waited with me for the arrival of this awful character. Like everyone else, Kate or my buddy Russell, there was little he could do. Just being there with us all was enough. By the weekend I had recovered sufficiently to drive Dave to the train which would take him on to his aeroplane and the journey home to his girlfriend in Spain. He really had been through a lot in this short visit and our comfortable relationship had been both restored and enriched. As we gathered his belongings a phone call came through. It was Sergeant Jackson again. I had forgotten all about him and the mystery of the blue Citroen Saxo.

'Good morning, Sir. An update on your complaint. I visited the registered keeper of the vehicle. As suspected she has no police connection at the present time. I have managed to ascertain that in her role as a senior social worker within children's services she was issued with some identity to enter Police Headquarters. It was this she used to give you the impression that she was a policewoman.'

By now I was remembering the previous call from this earnest Policeman.

'While visiting her home and upon reminder of the incident she appeared to be in a state of shock. She did apologise for the profanity that she proffered towards you, but impersonating a police officer and knowingly and falsely occupying a disabled parking space are both offences. How do you feel about proceeding?'

'I hope you don't mind, but I am recovering from cancer and in the scale of things it sounds as if she has had enough of a shock from your visit to sort things out.'

117

Sergeant Jackson agreed and just for a moment dropped his official manner.: 'I agree. You were right about the wrinkles too -blimey! I don't think we need to add to them. The best of luck with your recovery Sir and thanks for contacting us. Goodbye.'

As we drove to the station I recounted the incident to Dave and we enjoyed a good chortle. On the platform we exchanged a few jokes about our various scrapes with the police when we were younger. The announcer declared the train to be five minutes late. I had thought of something special to say to him at the last minute but couldn't manage it. Just like the time when he helped me buy the hat we clung on to each other as the train drew in. Neither of us spoke, both feeling somehow pleased with the events of recent days and optimistic about my prognosis. When we let go, his eyes were as full of water as were mine. Daft sod!

As he found his seat and sat down waving at me I would have paid anything to someone who could have immediately supplied me with a felt tip, a piece of paper and some blu-tac. Armed with these I could have scribbled out the message that I wanted him to hear. I could then have stuck it to the outside of his train window so that Dave and everybody else travelling in the train to Manchester that morning would know how well he had done.

Chapter 31

Throughout the previous chapters I have been able to refer to notes that I have collated over the months of my treatment. In addition to the art work, writing has proved to be a good therapy and helped me keep all of issues and incidents in some sort of perspective. In writing about the final month of this invasion, I find myself having to rely entirely upon memory - I had little interest in writing notes or reminders due to the problems that were occurring. For example, the sensory associations linked to my hospital treatment were taking a serious toll on my mental health. To my friends and family I may have appeared to be coping quite well. The truth was far from this. To gain four hours sleep for example was to become a luxury - I suffered from a recurring dream in those precious hours and it would wake me up in a total panic.

Each time the dream had the same build up. I had simply volunteered at the children's school to help on an outing in response to a brightly coloured poster asking for helpers. I thought nothing about the unusual fact that all four of my children, though all different ages were in the same class and all going on the same outing. On the morning of the trip, two double decker buses stood outside the school and my job for the day was allocated. My role was to sit in the second bus along with other parents and teachers. I was told to sit on the top deck in the front seat and use a remote control to drive and steer the bus in front. The bus in front contained all the children - including my four. The buses pulled away straight onto a motorway and the task seemed quite easy. I had to conentrate on the task ahead of me and safely steer the bus full of kids that was about a hundred yards ahead of me.

Only a couple of junctions went past on the motorway before we turned off and even though only a few miles from the children's school in Wakefield, we were now travelling along a perilous curving road through the valley of Glen Coe in spectacular Scottish mountain scenery. I had no time to look at the countryside. This is where my job as remote control driver became really difficult. Each time the kids bus in front of me turned a corner and was hidden from my view I had to guess which way to steer them using my remote control. When my bus caught up to the bend it was with a huge relief that I could see the kid's bus was still on the road. As each bend passed I knew that my luck would soon run out. This was emphasised by the sight of my four children and ten of their friends with their faces pressed hard against the back window - screaming in fear. With parents and teachers yelling advice at me eventually my luck did run out and I screamed in horror as I witnessed the kid's bus leave the road and launch into a sheer drop down a cliff. At this point I usually snapped out of my dream, making strange and frightened noises that also woke Kate. Any psychologist reading this would have an opinion as to what was going on in my mind. Even to my untrained brain the dream must have been the consequence of feeling out of control.

My obsession with the smell of soap in the house continued and I would hide the bottles wherever I could - in cupboards or behind towels. I visited the chemist and began the bizarre task of smelling out the least offensive bars of soap. I decided a brand called 'Pure and Simple' was the least smelly so bought a pile of these and lay one on each sink at home. Drinking water remained a problem too so I came upon the brilliant idea of watering it down. On one of my walks with Minnie I passed a lady who was just sat on a bench eating a sandwich made with white bread. This reminder of the refreshments trolley had an immediate reaction and a few yards later I was sick behind a conifer bush. In the walk from the park to my house which usually takes about five minutes, I was sick a further four times. More than anything else, I feared going back to the ward to continue the treatment. My much travelled road had become a 'Cul de sac' and I could see no way forward.

Under the pretence of needing some 'top up' medicine to cope with the side effects, I made an appointment at my local surgery to see one of the Doctors. The receptionist at our surgery is incredibly friendly and makes a huge effort. At any one of my visits there over these past months she has been kind, supportive encouraging and helpful. Whenever I have rung the surgery from home she has recognised my voice and helped me gain the most convenient appointment possible. As I was waiting for this particular appointment one of the other patients rose from his seat disgruntled about a problem and started shouting at her. I left my seat too;

'Don't be having a go at her, she is one of the best receptionists in the health service and you should be glad of it.'

The loud man backed down straight away and a hush descended over the waiting room. I like to think that I would have acted in the same way before I became ill though somehow I don't think so. In the Doctors room, I made a request for my prescription and hoped he would ask how I was getting along. He did. He asked about the family, about Kate, about my work and how we were managing financially. At the last minute he asked how I was feeling. With relief I went onto explain the feelings I had been getting about my remaining treatments, the associations and the fear of returning to the ward. I omitted to tell him that I had been giving serious consideration about diluting water with water in case he decided to 'section' me under the Mental Health Act. He drew his chair much closer to me, it was un-nerving, especially with the lamp that he had strapped to his forehead just an inch or two away from me.

He put a hand on each one of my knees and said 'The chemotherapy regime you are under is a frightening one. Believe me if I was on it I would be shit scared too.'

That little intrusion to my personal space really helped. He even gave me his mobile phone number and said that I could ring him anytime. I had no intention of doing that, my buddy Russell was already carrying out a great job on the phone whenever I needed to talk. I returned home slightly more self assured and waited for the fortnightly pattern to repeat itself again.

It wasn't the worst wait I have ever had. I suffered more as a fledgling single parent in the summer that my ex-wife left me. Another week of that terrible summer in 1993 had gone by. I was still on holiday and wondering how to occupy Sam and Rosie. Any parent finds the summer holidays a struggle to get through- that is quite usual. My main concern was to keep them so busy as not to miss their mum. It wasn't a very realistic goal. Rosie in particular had taken a turn for the worse. This normally lively and cheeky little girl was very sad. The spark had dissapeared and she would sit and play quietly alone which was very unlike her. I also found it difficult to find anything that she would eat, I couldn't even excite her with the idea of a day out on the beach which was an activity she had always enjoyed. Sam had on the other hand become rather stoic about the situation. Though only five years old he took on the mantle of becoming my mate. I recall wondering how to deal with this kind of relationship as I found it uncomfortable. He started calling me Pete instead of Dad and wanted to know what kind of jobs he could do to help me out. There was plenty to do, we had chickens, ducks, a cat, a dog and a rabbit. Together we drew out a picture of each animal on a chart – the pictures had a tick box next to them and this way he could record which animals he had fed. It worked well and drew Rosie into the daily jobs too.

One of our chickens had just hatched chicks; fourteen of them and Rosie began looking after them until 'Mother Hen' jealously pecked her on the leg. To this day Rosie has a terrible phobia about chickens

These worrying situations continued for too long and I eventually felt forced to telephone their mum to arrange a meeting to discuss the children - I managed to arrange some care for Sam and Rosie and hastily travelled off to meet her in a library car park. She was very upset about my description of the children's reaction to her leaving and soon decided to return to our house. That evening she did return and Sam and Rosie were obviously very pleased to see her back. They didn't actually express this very much but just accepted her return as the way that things should be. In fact we all just got on with a fairly typical family evening - a meal, a dog walk and a bath. Sam and Rosie did express their pleasure when she put them to bed. That awful sadness that surrounded Rosie lifted and Sam seemed more like a five year old again rather than a brave little tin soldier attending to his duties.

With the children in bed we had, at last, a couple of hours to talk about some of the things that had gone wrong in our marraige and the trouble that it had brought us. The heartfelt dicsussion went well and no blame was attached on either side. This was huge progress. At 10pm she decided to visit her new boyfriend to hand back the key to his flat. I insisted on taking the key for her but this didn't work. There was apparently something important she had to say to him and only she could say it..... so I watched her drive off, expecting her to be away an hour or two in order to say her goodbyes, collect her belongings and hand back his key.

It was a beautifully warm summer evening, the type of evening that occurs in this country just two or three times a year. I decided to set up a table in our courtyard and wait for her return. The air was still and there was no noise, no generator, just a few candles for company - there was not even enough wind to blow them out. I opened a bottle of wine. By 11pm I had set up a lantern on my kitchen table to compensate for the fading light and waited a bit longer. I then decided to cut out a twelve foot length of wall paper from an old roll of woodchip. I found the roll in a cupboard, cut out the required length and then, in dark green emulsion paint, daubed out the words *'Welcome Back'* right across it - I then fastened it to the gate posts at the entrance to our courtyard. Along with the candles, the lantern and a half finished bottle of wine it must have presented as a pleasant little scene and one that I hoped she would be pleased to come back to.

By midnight I was still expecting her to return. My wait continued another hour. I began to feel deflated and knew that the three hours she had already taken was too long a time to accomplish the task of saying goodbye to her lover. By two in the morning I had finished the bottle of wine and given up hope. The narrow road to the house was a long one and on a still night I could always hear a car long before it came into sight. As I began packing away I heard in the distance the sound of a car engine - gradually lights began to flicker amongst the hedgerows and eventually the sound of wheels was heard as they ploughed their way along the stream. Any rise in hope was smashed as the car that had appeared drove on past my driveway and entered the house of my only neighbour. It was their son coming back from a late night somewhere. With that I gave up, blew out the candles, tidied away the little table and moved off to bed. She was also in bed, but not with me.

I was soon asleep but awoke just two hours later, it was now 5am. I remembered my poster made from woodchip was still pinned across the gateway and thought how ridiculous it would look to my neighbour in the light of day. The postman may find it slightly offensive too. I dressed and went back outside and ripped it all away from the gateway along with any hopes of her coming back. The worst of this day was yet to come: Sam and Rosie had gone to bed happily - they had been read a story by their mum and drifted off to sleep. When they awoke at 7am she was nowhere to be seen and I had more bad news to break to the poor little buggers.

Later that morning I rang my brother Barry who lived alone down in the depths of France. I told him what a position we were in and how we needed to leave the house for a bit. By the next morning we were packed up and ready for France. We said goodbye to a few local friends who were to help feed all of the animals. The dog went to Sam and Rosie's mum in that sordid little flat she occupied with her lover and we set off. The drive from Scarborough to Dover was hard work – I was driving, navigating and feeding the children all on my own . Going on holiday for the first time without her was a new experience. I don't know how we managed it. I can hardly remember the actual drive at all.

On the other side of the channel we were driving along much quieter roads and well into a journey that had been refreshed by the hour long channel crossing. I noticed how messy the car had become and as luck would have it a service area called an 'Aire' came into view at the right time. I pulled over, we visited the loo, had a drink and cleaned out the car. I was pleased with my now tidy car which previously had been full of blankets, crisps, sleeping bags, pillows and drink bottles. With everything tidy I set off up the acceleration lane back onto the motorway. A large Citroen driving behind me started flashing his lights at me. The driver even bothered to overtake me on the acceleration lane. His animated gaelic expression and a finger pointing backwards forced me to take a look in the driver's mirror. All I had actually done with the sleeping bags, pillows and blankets was put them on my car roof, no wonder the inside of the car looked so neat. As I set off each of these things slid off the roof at various points between the service station and the motorway........

My eleventh treatment at the hospital proved no easier than at any other time. I still received all the help I needed and this time the reinforcements came in the shape of Kate's mum and dad. Bill and Stella had flown in from Ireland again. They helped Kate with the shopping, the cooking and looking after the kids throughout the fortnightly cycle. They did a great job too. With family like this to rely upon coping with Hodgkin's Lymphoma seemed a great deal less stressful than parking up on french motorway and leaving two children alone in a vulnerable car while I scurried around picking up bedding off the tarmac.

Chapter 32

My sister Pauline from Cornwall and her husband Andy were the helpers for my final treatment; the twelfth; the last of the six cycles! They had responded to another roll call from Kate and were glad to oblige. They had first been to help us when I was in hospital awaiting diagnosis. Though they have been married for a while now I hardly knew Andy apart from meeting him at a wedding or more recently at my Dad's funeral. We had also spoken on the phone a few times, though never for very long. I am not keen on long phone conversations and not aware of any bloke that is. Kate can talk for ages on the phone, especially to my sister. Of all the friends and family that have helped populate my tiny empire the only person I speak to over a long period of time on the phone is Ian, the friend who bought me the art materials at the beginning of my treatment. We both like a good moan and are prepared to tolerate each other's rantings for over an hour.

Andy, however, was a bit of a stranger to me but during their visit I began to feel sorry that we did live so far apart. He and Pauline provided the proverbial bacon sandwiches, the tow rope and the hot flask. Kate substituted the telephone for the settee and gained lots of support from Pauline while Andy's personality managed to apply an atmosphere of calm to the house. Michael and Joe enjoyed his company too. He suffers from something called Fibromyalgia and is never quite sure how his illness will effect him from day to day so understood the concept of 'pacing' which is something I have yet to master. It also turned out that he is a Reiki practitioner and a spiritual healer. He offered to help me by using these skills if I felt ever it would be useful - I wasn't too keen, to be honest.

My final treatment was to be real milestone for me but two days before this I had to attend the ward for my final injection. My fears about the few days ahead were all too obvious. The nursing team could see that I was very unsettled - it was nothing personal and they understood that. It wasn't an entirely physical reaction on my part either; the build up of associations which manifested themselves through my sense of smell had become unbearable. Recognising my plight, Catherine took me into the side room and made sure that I had some privacy. She helped me settle me down to a point in time so I could take this small injection into my stomach. If this comparatively simple procedure was so traumatic - how would the chemotherapy effect me? I decided that I wouldn't be able to turn up for the last chemotherapy treatment. My body was telling me it would be one too many – it was telling me enough was enough. I kept this to myself and left the ward feeling slightly guilty that I had taken the injection with no intention of adhering to the care plan ahead of me.

During the next two days if I had have been given fifty pence every time somebody said 'just one more' I would have had £11.50 in my pocket. I felt like screaming at each one of the people that offered these helpful encouragements. Only one person, my mate Norman, in straightforward Geordie style said 'I know you feel this one is one too many, I know you feel it will be no easier than the last eleven put together. Do your best.' How did he know that? I pondered this for some time. I can only imagine it was because his wife has Non-Hodgkins Lymphoma, a very unusual type and together they must spend a lot of time watching, waiting and wondering what the future will bring. In many ways my lymphoma is preferable. It is the type that requires a defined and specific programme of drugs and though hard to endure the treatment had been progressing very well. I changed my mind and would do my best and turn up on Wednesday. It would feel as if I had let so many people down otherwise - all the people who had populated my tiny empire over the last eight months.... all of those who

ensured the boundary walls had been kept intact.... a¹
who had helped to defend the walls from my invader..

As Pauline drove me into the hospital, I sat quietly in the passengᴄ
seat trying to control the sweeping nausea that built up as we neared
the car park. She spoke only when I did and understood that it
was to be a quiet journey. For the last time a parking space was
found. The entrance was entered, the pyjama clad smokers
smoked, the volunteer volunteered, the phone box phoned, the
stairs performed as they always did, the doors opened and the anti
bacterial gel made me feel even sicker. The fifty yard corridor
extending to the nurses' station looked to be a mile long. The tiny
nurses in the distance waved. As I neared them one of the nurses
gave me a hug. 'I wondered if we would see you today' she said 'it
feels as if we are beating you up.'

She was dead right. I steeled myself for the four bags of drugs
ahead of me. In an unexpected and vivid hallucination I climbed
between the ropes of a boxing ring. My frail body limped into the
ring as I looked down below at the canvas that would bear my first
fall. As I raised my eyes, looming over me was a huge boxer
rubbing his gloves together. He wore a brown bag over his head,
identical in all but size to the bags that covered my drugs on the
drip stand. Two eye holes in the bag revealed a dark menacing
stare. He was smooth and sweaty with strength rippling from every
muscle. He smiled with a smug satisfaction at the forthcoming
damage he would inflict. Catherine, who had swapped her nurse's
uniform for a bikini also climbed in with me; a promoter handed
her a large sign which she showed to a crowd on all sides of the
ring.

*'Go twelve rounds with Captain Chemo. Huge prizes for the
survivor!'*

129

The bell rang - my final round was underway. Catherine got out of the way and I could see no referee. The only company I had was Captain Chemo and a bucket to be sick in, he took a few steps towards me and set about his brutal task.

Pauline of course had no idea about the macabre scene I was visualising. I sensed she was in a state of shock when she took her position in the ringside seat. There is nothing like the thought of somebody else in distress to pull you around and I managed to force the image of the huge boxer away from my mind. I was left with the reality of the side room, the over-hanging television and the rattle of the drugs trolley. Only the brown bags that still covered the drugs reminded me of the fearsome Captain Chemo.

Kate arrived later in the day to relieve Pauline and help me through the worst of the punches. As always her presence assured me that the treatment would soon end as she would be there when I woke up. When I came round I remember telling her how much I loved her as she busily sat me up and tied my shoe laces. She and Laura supported my dizzy frame as we left the side room for the last time. I can't remember too much about those final minutes with the nursing team. I do remember how pleased they were that I had survived all twelve rounds. I also remembered somebody commenting that this had been the first treatment when I hadn't been sick all over the place. I felt sure they would be pleased to see me and my various reactions leave their ward. I must have been hard work for them. I left the ward with Kate and on the way up the long corridor I looked to my left at the other patients receiving their drugs from the drip stands looming above their Shackleton chairs. I hung on to Kate as we looked forward to completing our usual stumble through the hospital and meeting the fresh air that would help my recovery.

We walked twenty yards past the usual gaggle of smokers when the experiences of the last eight months came back to me in a sudden rush. The outdoor bench where I had sat with my visitors was empty and waiting right in front of us. Kate sat me down on the bench. Normally she would walk off and fetch the car, but not this time, she just sat and held my hand. The enormity of the achievement hit me hard. In the car park, sat on this bench I tried hard to control my emotions as Kate held on tightly. It wasn't the effects of the chemotherapy, it wasn't the memory of so many treatments, or the kindness and skill of the nurses: I felt as proud of getting through this as of anything else I had ever done in my life.

Six months earlier when cancer first invaded my tiny empire, I had visited my local café still reeling from the effects of my first treatment. I even left the café without paying for my drink. Today I am sitting in the same café writing and remembering. Two things have changed. This is no longer a story of my illness or my experiences, it is a love story. Kate has co-ordinated a whole system of resistance for me. In spite of everything this vulnerable woman has picked me up and lifted me home, bathed me and calmed me. She has looked on my diminishing frame, my bald head and my sad eyes and never faltered in her devotion to care. She has organised my medicines, listened to my fears and nursed me through the night. She has safeguarded our children, given us all optimism and protected me from infection. That is why this is now a love story. What is the other thing to have changed? Oh yes - the café owner now asks me to pay for my coffee before I drink it!

"Ceasefire"

Chapter 33

The recovery period following my final chemotherapy proved to be much longer than ever before and the side effects were more draining. It reinforced my opinion that the last one had, after all, been too much for me. Two full days at least were spent alone in the bedroom managing the unwelcome side effects. I was glad that Kate and the boys had company downstairs and I did eventually accept the offer of a Reiki session some three or four days into Pauline and Andy's visit. The alien was behaving at his very worst and perhaps this would surprise him. The Reiki session was to prove very different to those I had been given at the hospice - this time it was in my own bed and in a position that I felt comfortable with. The birdsong station on the radio chirped away while Andy hovered somewhere around me, near me and with me. Within a few minutes of the session starting the alien gave up and let me sleep. I remember waking up sometime later alone and relaxed. No nausea to resist, just an appreciation of the silence within my body and the peaceful hum of birdsong. It stayed like that for nearly an hour - not long perhaps but an hour off in the middle of a three day battle campaign can be regarded as a life saver.

Another film moment cropped up in that peaceful sixty minutes. It was from 'Zulu' the frontier battle against the Zulu tribe who were attacking the fort at Rork's Drift. Michael Caine played the lieutenant and Stanley Baxter, as the engineer, were the commanding officers. A film that portrayed the British stiff upper lip at its best value. In truth I felt more sorry for the Zulus who were protecting their own land and therefore more likely to be in the right than the British. During the pitch battle the chief called his huge tribe of warriors to retreat from the fort.

The redcoats were shocked to be granted the unexpected respite. On gathering themselves they were ordered to rebuild their boundary fences and report to parade for a roll call to assess the casualties. The Sergeant Major grunted out their names one by one and waited for a response. If there was none then he made a strike through the name on his sheet. 'Hitch.' He shouted. No reply. 'Hitch, you are alive' he stated, 'I have seen you.'
'Am I Sir?' Hitch replied.

The Zulus continued their barrage of the fort with renewed energy soon after this roll call had ended. So did my enemy; the alien. Despite my hatred of this character and all he had brought to me, despite the profanity I used in my conversations with him and the effect he was having upon me, I had the wonderful knowledge that this time he would not be coming back. This was his final assault on my mental and physical health. He decided to go out with a bang. He normally leaves me quite quickly but this time he hung on until the following Monday. Like the Zulu chief in the film, who loitered on the horizon, the alien's head and body would once more appear mischieviously on the sky line, still in full battle dress. It was if he had become quite fond of me and found it difficult to leave. Don't expect me to say that I felt the same, I had no such pretensions and couldn't wait to see him gone forever. He waved his spear slowly in an arc across his head and at last jogged off - his wobbling battle feathers were the last I was to ever see of him. For the final time I shouted out a message to the now empty skyline 'Sod off and don't come back.' I hoped my insult hit him loud and hard in the back of the head. I watched the horizon for a bit longer, he was definitely gone.

A day later I was back in the land of the living and at the hospice finishing my painting of the Kingfishers. I had once believed that the hospice would be the very last place I wanted to be. Since that time I had been regularly arriving for my sessions once or twice a week. With my chemotherapy now over I felt very strange - no more injections.... no more back pain.... no more brown bags of medicine.... no more side room.... no more side effects. My next blood test and scan to confirm the progress was at least five weeks away.

Apart from the art group and the reiki sessions, the really important part of each visit was the chat going on between people who had suffered the many different types of cancer. They had each endured the different types of chemo' or radiotherapy needed to improve their survival chances. On one occasion I was sitting next to a lady who had undergone extensive treatment for breast cancer. As we painted, I dared to admit to her that I felt in a kind of limbo now the ward treatment was over. Never moving the paint brush away from her work she replied, 'Talk to anyone here who has been through that treatment. They will all say the same, you can't wait for it to be over and when it is, there is a great hole in your life.'

That is how it felt and that is how it developed. A week later it had become more than a hole in my life, I felt completely lost. The hospice at least provided a resting place where I could reflect on the events of the last year. I thought about my Grandad who had died at the age of ninety six. He and my Grandmother had even celebrated their sixtieth wedding anniversary – it had been a grand long life. He was a modest fellow and rarely spoke of his time in the Great War. As his grandchildren we discovered quite a lot about his war years as he recounted some of his adventures for a local school project. At that time he was in his eighties:-

He had been wounded at Arras in Northern France as he and his chums left their trench to attack the enemy machine guns. He spoke of the number of paces he took across that field, watching those

134

around him drop to the ground and wondering when it would be his turn. Luckily the bullet that hit him was too low to mark him as another fatality, instead it went right through his knee. He recalled how he fell onto that field, how he checked the damage and soon realised that his active part in this battle was over. At that point he dragged himself across the muck and dropped into a mortar hole and began a long wait. He had to wait a short time for the fighting to end, but a much longer time before he was discovered alive in that hole. The teacher at the school recorded my Grandad on a his cassette player. As he spoke, Grandad didn't even know his words were being engraved onto a reel of magnetic tape. It was a very natural and humorous account of the situation he was in. At one point he discussed the hours he spent lying injured and waiting to be rescued:

'The trench we had jumped from had been our home for three days and was a mucky stinky place - I was glad to get out. The machine guns we were trying to reach didn't look like they would provide us with any comfort either. Thanks to that bullet I ended up in a place that belonged to nobody. I had nothing to do for anybody, just relax, look at the sky and wait for something to happen.'

I would be horrified to think that I could even contemplate comparing the bravery he showed then to the time I have spent in my 'post-chemo, clean and clinical trench.' I can relate to the feeling of being in 'no man's land' though. I didn't want to go backwards, I was glad that I hadn't to go any further and even more pleased that I hadn't kicked the bucket. Thinking about him lying in the mortar hole watching the sky and clutching his bleeding knee made me appreciate the fact that I now had a few weeks to get used to the ceasefire, wait for something to happen, try to relax and enjoy this hole in my life.

Chapter 34

It was time for a project; nothing too adventurous - I had no intention of cycling coast to coast across the Pennines or riding my motorbike around the coastline of the United Kingdom. My energy levels wouldn't allow me to even get my bike out of the garage! I needed something local that wouldn't cost much. A much smaller challenge was needed and it came in the form of a garden shed. This winter had made an impact on us all in that we at last had snow. My lads were delighted. At the ages of nine and eleven they had never seen real snow and two days off school made sure that they both enjoyed and played in it. At that time I put an advert in the shop window

Have you a shed that is misbehaving? I am willing to take it away and re-home it when the snow is over. Phone Pete.

I hoped nobody would ring too soon and began to think of some other things that I could do. By now the country was in financial meltdown. As taxpayers, we were the unwilling paymasters ploughing millions, no billions into the banks bailing them away from the consequences of their greed. My own finances had dried up too, luckily I had been given four months full pay by my employers and four months at half pay. This financial cushion was over and we were living off the money that Kate and I had saved to replace the central heating boiler. I sent a letter off to Gordon Brown out of courtesy really. I expressed some dismay at the state we were in as a nation and went on to inform him that as he was relying so heavily on the tax payer, it was only fair to inform him that I was no longer paying any. The reply would be long awaited.

The housing market had collapsed too. I didn't think I had any part to play in this one until I noticed all the 'To Let' signs that littered the local streets. All people who had given up trying to sell their houses and were trying to recoup some cash. For a couple of weeks I spent idle minutes putting the letter 'I' on these 'to let signs', so it read 'toilet.' Not very amusing really though Michael and Joe enjoyed accompanying me on these mischievous errands. It was in fact quite a complex task as the added letter had to conform with the colour and shape of the various estate agents' signs. A third week on this task was saved when the phone rang again.

'Is that Pete? We have a shed that has outgrown the garden. We need it shifting, what do you think?'

Here would be my project. As mentioned before, not exactly a race to the South Pole or anything remotely heroic, but still a challenge. Prior to my illness it would have been just a job for a Saturday. It was different now and would be a great challenge. I went to visit the shed with a hammer and a set of spanners. The shed was large enough for my needs and I realised this was going to take me some time. It needed dismantling, shifting, a new roof and rebuilding. I would do just a little bit at a time which was fine with the shed owners who didn't need it moving straight away. It was also a great relief for the local estate agents and Gordon Brown - all of whom wouldn't be bothered again.

Chapter 35

The art of pacing yourself is a subtle one. I have a friend called David who had to leave work early due to ill health. I have known him for years, working alongside him at Huddersfield University on the teacher training programmes. I have been pleased to see the gradual improvement in his health and increased levels of energy. Like so many others he and his wife Marion have been very supportive during these months. He sent me an article on 'pacing' to help my recovery:- the idea is that when you feel well enough you bank some of your energy into an account, you then draw upon that account when the energy levels are low. I found this sound common sense advice hard to accept. On a good day, especially if Kate was at work, I would put my energy levels well into the unauthorised overdraft. I would walk the dog, then do some shopping, set off down to the allotment to do some weeding, make some tea for us all and maybe play a game of football in the park with Michael and Joe. The phone call from the bank manager was inevitable and the next day would be spent limping around, exhausted and forced to sit down and ponder upon my excesses.

Joe's birthday was approaching just three weeks after my final chemotherapy session and I began to worry about it. I had booked a sports hall for an hour's football and Joe had invited eleven friends. As the date approached I knew I wasn't up for it and it would have been too disappointing to rearrange the football party for a more sedate event. Regardless of the pacing theory, Kate and I had shared an understanding that we would do our best to keep the boys activities as normal as possible. Badminton and music for Michael and football for Joe. Kate had already developed her interest in sport in ways that had thoroughly surprised me and I admired this. Due to my overly zealous use of the 'energy account' the sports hall and the subsequent party at our house was going to deepen the overdraft.

One asset I had managed to bank was a memory of all the people who had made a general offer of help without really knowing what they could do. These offers had come from people that I didn't know very well and were usually made in the school playground as I waited for the boys to come out of class. One such offer came a month earlier from Malcolm who I knew to be a football coach. Before the football party arrived I had a quick chat with his wife who I met in the school playground and Malcolm's offer of help was confirmed. Before I knew it he had rung me, discussed the hour in the sports hall, assured me of a successful time and said he was looking forward to it. That is exactly what happened. The most energetic thing I had to do was help pick up a few cones and keep score for the match. Kate was freed up to get on with the food at home and prepared for twelve hungry kids to arrive. Malcolm didn't even come back for a beer, he just tidied up all the coloured vests and the training balls, put everything in a huge net and went off to see his own football team where he was due to carry out a coaching session later that afternoon.

There have been many disadvantages to this illness and staying with the banking analogy these can be seen as the 'withdrawals' from my energy account. At times the withdrawals are taken from the dispenser three or four times a day, day after day. It is hard to stop yourself asking for a 'print out' of the situation. This self inflicted pain reveals a mini-statement of the overdraft that exists. The overdraft is bigger than feared. As my eye reluctantly dropped down the long list of payments I recalled the fact that there are still payments outstanding - huge calls on my energy and perseverance that can't be avoided. Suddenly the statement comes up with a nice surprise and reveals a credit! There it sits in black and white

- a fact that can't be disputed. It brings the account back into the black and enables you to be much less worried about the forthcoming demands. The depositor is listed and there are the names; Malcolm and Joanne, Norman and Louise, Rick and Lynn, Anthony and Catherine, Ian and Bev, Dennis and Kay, the list could go on and does.

The deposits these creditors made into my energy account are all different. They may have been small regular amounts on a standing order or a single larger 'one off' payment. The size of their deposit doesn't matter, they are all from people who just wanted to contribute in some way. All of these deposits have been accepted. It has been a great account and you couldn't get a better interest rate anywhere. The Hodgkin's Lymphoma has been a huge drain on our family and our resources, but our lives are richer for it.

Chapter 36

There were still two weeks to go before my next scan and the feeling of being in 'no mans land' continued. This time I was waiting for a Cat Scan which stands for Computerised Axial Tomography. Dozens of X- rays at all angles to the body are put through a computer which produces a layered three dimensional image of the whole body. After it had been explained to me I kept thinking of the bread slicing machine at the bakers which I expected produced a similar result. It is this process that would tell my consultant if there had been any relapse of the condition. I felt very optimistic about the forthcoming scan and the results.

As with all things people react differently when discovering an illness in their body. During the course of all this I have met people who had acquired so much knowledge about their condition it was almost like speaking to a doctor. These are the 'must knows.' - what a boring bunch they are too! Others are prepared to let the doctors take full control and want no information about it at all - these are the 'don't want to knows.' I can understand both points of view, if I had to make a choice between the two types then I veered towards the latter group. Once I had been given my diagnosis I found it difficult to read the information about Hodgkins Lymphoma that the hospital had given me. Anything I did read wouldn't seep into my knowledge or understanding almost as if somewhere in my sub consciousness a road block had been set up. Gradually the need to gain some information became easier and I manoeuvred my stubborn brain around the blockage at a careful and deliberate pace. I went no faster than I wanted to and certainly not at the pace that many would have expected.

We visited Kate's family in South West Cork a few years back and took the car on the ferry from Swansea to Cork. What an eventful journey that was. Firstly I left Kate and the children in their cabin late one evening and went off on a mission to give our dog a drink. That was a difficult task as she was in a kennel somewhere down on the car deck. The complex challenge that lay ahead of me felt very achievable due to the wine that Kate and I had quaffed in the ship's restaurant. The first part was easy, I went to reception on the boat and just asked to be given access to the kennels so I could give my dog a drink. The young lady was about to refuse me this access when another inebriated passenger who had overheard my request decided that it would be a great idea to give his dog a drink too. With two requests now to deal with the young lady relented and called one of the crew to open up the car deck. He did so and meticulously counted us down. There were only two of us but he made an accurate job of it! All went well, I found my kennel fairly quickly; the dog wasn't thirsty after all and I wondered why I had become so concerned as to think she may have needed a drink. She even looked at me with that 'what are you doing here' expression. I had no idea if the other passenger had received a similar reaction from his pet. Anyway he had disappeared. I went upstairs to the exit only to find it locked. The crewman had already counted us dog lovers back up the stairs then locked the huge door and left. If there had been twenty three of us I could have understood his mistake. As it was I was now alone on this car deck along with two hundred cars, forty containers lorries, twelve motorhomes, eight lovely motorbikes and six dogs, none of whom seemed thirsty.

I shouted out in vain for a long time wondering if Kate had woken in the cabin - if so she would have panicked and declared me missing. This could be to my advantage but the more likely outcome would be an expectation that I had gone overboard. I carried on shouting. It seemed hopeless. I tried to get some sleep on this drafty iron stairwell and this was even more hopeless. I had sobered up by this time - it was about one 'o' clock in the morning and decided to bash the door with the heel of my shoe and this is where I struck lucky. Yet another late night drunk in the foyer outside of the car deck door had been struggling to tie his shoelaces up. As he bent down to attempt his laces one more time he heard the muffled beating of my shoe through the thick metal. He reported it, bless him, and I was soon let out. Kate thankfully had not woken in my absence - I crept into the bunk bed and felt glad that there had been no disaster and would be just a jolly tale to tell over breakfast.

On driving the car away from the boat I was still trying to calm Kate down and wishing I had never informed her of the previous night's adventure when we came across a sign outside a village just a couple of miles from the ferry.

Road ahead closed. Access denied, except for traffic

It was confusing alright and I was glad of it as the conversation then wandered away from my nocturnal dog-watering obsession quite naturally. Later in the journey we stopped in a lay-by for a breather and watched a man in a van parked about twenty yards ahead of us. He carefully took out a ladder and mounted it against a post. At the top of the post it read:

Accident black spot. This was followed by a large black spot painted onto the sign and a bit more writing which informed us: *27 deaths in 2003.*

As we watched, the chap took a number of plastic laminated numbers from the van and started climbing his ladder. I have never

143

before seen the figures on these signs actually being changed. (When all the red phone boxes disappeared from our communities there were never any witnesses.) As I watched this fellow climb the ladder I wondered what poor soul had recently befallen a fatality on this stretch of road. I was absolutely staggered when he replaced the number '7' with a '6.' It now informed us only 26 people had died there - somebody had recovered! Perhaps they had woken from a coma or even bounced back to life in the chapel of rest. It was good news anyway - I am sure the family were delighted. It was the type of information you would only get in Ireland.

I mention these events as they are loosely connected with my reluctance to face up to the situation I was in. It was slightly crazy to take up the view that I didn't need any information on Hodgkin's Lymphoma, crazier than trying to water my dog on a car deck in the middle of the night. I didn't need to know everything like the 'must know' crowd, but 'some' knowledge would have helped me cope with the events to follow. That night on the ferry the crewman had counted two of us down to the kennels and only one returned. That reminded me of what happened to the lady in hospital with Hodgkin's disease. She had been the only other person I had known with the same condition as me. Just like my fellow passenger on the dog-watering mission, we had shared the same objective - just before she disappeared.

When I eventually realised I was in big trouble locked in that car deck I started banging my shoe on the door and eventually I was heard. The reactions I had suffered following the chemotherapy were weighing very heavily on me, but I had not been prepared to admit this, not even to Kate. Instead of hollering for help I just tried to get some sleep on a drafty iron staircase. None of this worked very well. The road block and the confusing sign about 'access to traffic' now makes perfect sense: The road block I had put up inside my own head had to come down. I could deny access as long as I wanted but traffic had to come through if I was going to get to the other side of this place. As for the man in the van with the sign - well there are some things that happen in Ireland that are just unexplainable and this should remain one of them. It is the charm of the place and is an example of a life that is far removed from the pompous carry on we have in England. If I am pushed, then I could say that there was a similarity - the sign could have read:

Cancer Black spot. 1,500 Hodgkins cases in 2009.

At that point my consultant drove into the lay by and jumped out of his van – looking firstly at my scan results he then shimmied up the pole to reduce the number by one. Knowing my consultant the idea of him climbing up a pole was unlikely. A positive result from my next scan didn't seem such a remote possibility.

Chapter 37

Somehow information about Lymphoma has managed to seep its way through my stubbornness and into my knowledge bank. I can say that in most cases this knowledge has been of benefit to me. Sometimes too much information is not a good idea. The Lymphoma Association sends out a quarterly newsletter which is a very well written source of news. It is produced in plain and simple English and includes many stories and experiences of the people who have been through this life changing condition. Just like the cards and letters that constantly popped through my letterbox I could open the newsletter whenever I felt like doing so. I didn't feel as confident about attending the association's annual conference in York, it was in May and Kate had booked places for us both. This, I felt, would be quite difficult to cope with though I had no idea why.

I understand now that Lymphomas are cancers of the lymphatic system and this is a system that we need to fight infection. The lymphatic system also helps with absorbing fat and vitamins from the digestive system. The usual sign of a lymphoma is a lump maybe in the neck, groin or armpit. In my case I never really felt these as they were well hidden and quite deep down. In some people the lumps are easier to spot and feel.

There are lots of symptoms too. I felt really tired for several months before I was diagnosed and couldn't shake off a flu like feeling. High temperatures were really worrying at the time and the scale of the night sweating was something that I wouldn't have believed possible. I wasn't dieting but still lost weight often as much as four or five pounds in a single night time. Other symptoms I have heard about include itching, stomach pains and a cough that won't go away. In many ways these are very common symptoms for lots of people. It is easy to see why a doctor may say 'You are suffering from a virus, there are some pretty nasty ones about at the moment, if it doesn't shift in two weeks, come back and we will have another look at you.'

Does this sound familiar? I was told this two or three times in the months leading up to my collapse!

The actual lymphoma happens when some white blood cells called lymphocytes, produced in the lymph nodes, become cancerous. These cells are usually helping your immune system so when they grow out of control the chances of fighting off infection are poor. As far as I know the causes of this are unknown. Following a biopsy of a lump in my neck I was diagnosed as having Hodgkin's Lymphoma. The staff in hospital took nearly a week to come back with the news that I was one of about fifteen hundred new cases of this disease each year. It often crops up in young people and the recovery rates are very good if you are diagnosed with it early on in your life. The recovery rates are not so high later in life and this is probably due to the fact that someone of my age could well have other problems like heart or chest conditions all of which make the chemotherapy treatment hard to take.

The other type of Lymphoma is for anything that is not diagnosed as Hodgkin's and surprisingly enough they are all labelled together as Non-Hodgkin's Lymphoma. There about ten thousand new cases each year. There are so many types of this and I felt very confused about the different labels attached to them. I would often be talking to somebody about my condition and he or she would recognise the name - most people know somebody who has had a lymphoma. One of my friends has a type where no treatment is needed, she just has to 'watch and wait' for changes. There is a lot of confusion between the different types and it is understandable.

I am reluctant to know more than this, I am sure that a little knowledge can be misleading unless you are entirely sure you know what you are talking about.

Looking back if I had known that there was a type of cancer that could be recognised by such a specific set of symptoms I would have asked the doctor for a blood test, rather than just carrying on at work hoping I would feel better. By the time the diagnosis had been made the condition was well advanced and had been for some time. Anybody can suffer any of these symptoms at any time for any reason; fatigue, losing weight, temperatures, sweating. These are all consequences of living a normal life. If you are reading this and can identify with any number of these symptoms don't be fobbed off with the virus explanation, as I was. Insist on a blood test. There are fours stages of lymphoma, I was at stage four when my treatment started. If I had listened to my body, instead of the useless advice I had received, then the treatment could have started earlier and probably have been less intense.

Chapter 38

Just before Christmas in 1993 I made a significant journey from my new home in Wakefield. Life without my first wife was taking shape well - Sam and Rosie had settled into their new schools, Kate had come to know them well and we were all getting on together. The future looked a bit brighter. Still the events of the previous summer left me full of uncertainty, I was in danger of messing up my new relationship with Kate and felt determined to face my problems full in the face. I borrowed a car and journeyed to Filey where my first wife was now living with the rock star. There was quite some surprise when I arrived late in the evening. Just entering the house where they lived was traumatic enough and we shared a tense cup of tea over polite chat about the children, their new house and plans for Christmas.

Here was another occasion very similar to the story of gaining access to the car deck on the ferry journey to Ireland. I was on unfamiliar ground, not sure why I was there and without an achievable objective. Sam and Rosie were the main focus for me and I confused them both with my message. I was saying that unless we sat down and sorted out our new and separate lives then the children would face all sorts of difficulties over the coming years. I wasn't very clear judging by the look on the two blank faces staring at me. It occurred to me that neither of them wanted to sit down and sort anything out - they wanted a new and separate life! The rock star was very reluctant to let my wife and I have any time together but I ended up walking around the block with her a couple of times. If you need a serious talk with somebody and don't like eye contact while you are doing it then walking is a great way to proceed. After thirty minutes of this I came to the conclusion that she was very uncertain about her future but the new life she was experiencing with the rock star was more exciting than the life she had had with me. I walked her back to the gate of her house and drove back down the A64 to Wakefield, it was two days before Christmas and nearly midnight.

Halfway home on an almost empty stretch of the road I saw headlights in my mirror approaching fast - very fast. A car was about to overtake me doing over a hundred miles per hour. The next ten seconds would be devastating as there was no room for him - an approaching car was to see to that. All three cars hit each other at the same time. I shut my eyes and remember thinking that my time had come. I didn't feel as if I had been crushed or anything had been cut off I just sat there while the car spun around a few times, hit something hard and my borrowed car ended up in a field next to the crumpled wreck of the speeding vehicle. I was surprised to find my legs and everything else intact and managed to get out of the badly bent door as quickly as I could.

A hundred yards away there was the sorry sight of a wrecked Peugeot and the sound of a woman wailing. The car next to me contained the crushed figures of two young lads, both completely unconscious and trapped. The car's bonnet was squeezed into a mangled mess and the steering wheel was lodged into the drivers chest stapling him to his seat. All that appeared to be working was the radio cassette which was belting out the Meatloaf album 'Bat out of Hell 2' - the actual song was 'Paradise By The Dashboard Light' and it was playing very loud. I couldn't do anything but try and wake them. There was no response. There was a smell of petrol and the ignition was still on - I managed to turn the ignition off and Meatloaf stopped singing. I ran the long distance up to the Peugeot dodging pieces of car engine as I did so. There was a similar scene of devastation - an unconscious driver and a lady passenger also trapped but awake and hysterical. She screamed at me to get her husband out. I could see that there was no point in trying. I stayed with her until I was joined by a throng of customers from a nearby pub who had heard the collision.

The firemen and ambulances soon arrived by which time the shock had kicked in, I was shaking quite vigourously as I sipped a hot cup of tea in the lounge bar of the pub. I remember refusing a large brandy that was thrust in front of my face. I needed to go and check the state of my car and wobbled off into the field where I had left it. By now the two lads had been cut away from their seats and were on the way to hospital. I looked at the Mazda I had been driving. It had been lent to me for the evening by my friends Jill and Craig and now it was in a field and in a right mess. There was a fireman with a torch next to the car looking in hedges.

'Hello.' I said. It distracted him from his search. 'What are you looking for?'
'The driver of this vehicle' he replied without really looking up.
'That will be me then.'

With that he pointed his torch at me, walked up closer and slowly shone the torch over my body. He then shone the torch at Jill and Craig's car which was a write off.
'You're a lucky beggar' he said.
With that he took me off to the ambulance for a check up. Not a scratch! Rather unsympathetically the ambulance crew handed me over to the police who breathalysed me straight away. The large brandy I had refused just ten minutes earlier would have turned the test positive. That was a piece of pure good fortune on this sorry night.

I made a couple of phone calls from the pub - one to Jill and Craig in Wakefield and one to Kate in Leeds. Not surprisingly at 1 am there was no answer. I was still nearer Filey than Wakefield so I rang the number that belonged to my wife and her boyfriend to see if they could help, By that time she had consumed several drinks in an effort to help recover from my visit and the only option was for her boyfriend to come and rescue me. It took an age for him to arrive due to all the road blocks caused by the accident.

When he did arrive I asked him to take me to Kate's house in Leeds. Once the conversation about the accident was over the remaining journey was a quiet one. I sat there and thought about two questions. Firstly, how did I manage to come out of that without a single injury? Secondly, at the end of this particular journey how was I going to express my gratitude to the driver that came to rescue me? He was the last person in the world I wanted to be with - he had messed up my life yet there he was sat next to me and doing me a big favour.

Chapter 39

My third week in no man's land was a very pleasant experience for my little body. Usually at this time I would be wincing and waiting in preparation for the injections, the chemotherapy, its reactions, the side effects and most of all the visit from the alien. This time nothing happened, there was no more treatment, no force to be reckoned with. I was accompanied only by silence. It was a total contrast to those long seconds I had experienced, during the accident on the A64, as I waited for the impact of metal on metal. Nothing actually did happen and this was a real shock to my system.

Recently I was driving home from work and approached a bend. As I got there a car screeched around it. I didn't know what car it was or who was driving it - I just remember it was red. There was no time to use my horn or brake, the red car lost control and came onto my side of the road. I couldn't do much but turn my steering wheel towards the pavement, shut my eyes and wait for the bang. Nothing happened, I opened my eyes, my car was on the pavement but somehow the collision had been avoided. The joy of missing out on an accident that seemed inevitable was a real surprise and explains how I felt in this third week. None of the trouble, none of the hassle - I just needed to drive my car off the pavement.

While the going was good we decided to pay a social visit to the nursing team on the Dr. Jackson ward. I was unsure how to express my appreciation for all they had done. Nothing I could think of would do the job properly. I decided to take bottles of wine along with me rather than the chocolates or flowers that were so often noticed on the ward. Kate and I entered the building with no other reason but to say 'hello', deliver the wine and leave a few minutes later. This time the corridor looked to be about fifty yards long.

That took me by surprise, last time I came it was nearly half a mile long and the nurses were just tiny figures in the distance. Had there been alterations? Just as normality was returning I passed the treatment room where the chemotherapy was being dispensed to four or five patients. I recognised two of them. There was a brief acknowledgement and I had an urge to go in and chat. I chose not to do so; the smell of the medicine hit me hard again. The smell invaded me, took up a large spoon and gave my stomach a good vigorous stir. I walked ten yards towards the nurses feeling very guilty that I had been unable to pop in and say hello to my chums in the treatment room.

I was lucky, the majority of the team that had looked after me were on shift that day and a few minutes were spent in welcome and listening to their comments about how well I was looking. I felt very emotional and very fortunate to be stood there talking to this team of specialists. That was okay. I had it under control - just agree, smile, share a few hugs, deliver the wine and walk calmly out of there. Only one nurse that I really wanted to see was missing from the group - it was Laura. Within a minute or two she had also made an appearance. As she neared, I tightened up. In just a couple of seconds a complicated process was complete. It started deep in my stomach, it rushed through every related organ and then burst out of my eyes. I was so pleased to see her but that made no difference as I tried my best to contain the emotion that enveloped me as she approached. I have no recollection of anything else that was said. I remember Laura put her had on mine which was by now firmly buried in my pocket. She squeezed my hand in my pocket, she understood why I had no words for her and the visit was over.

Chapter 40

The shed project continued. Personally, it was an important task to achieve but it was too hard to attempt on my own. I couldn't lift any of the sections; they were too heavy - my energy account would be in overdraft again. At least three people would be needed. The offer of assistance made in the playground, once again, proved to be the answer. Dominic is somebody I speak to at church sometimes. Of all the people I know they fall broadly into two groups: There are many like Dominic or Catherine or Gillian or Steve the fireman, who made a definite move as I stood about in the school playground. This group were always keen to ask how I was progressing with the treatment, ask about the family, put their arm across my shoulders and offer help.

'Don't forget, if there is anything I can do, just ask.' It meant such a lot.

Then, there was the group that knew I was ill. They made enquiries, on the quiet about me, especially when my hair fell out. Yet as I stood just a few yards away from them, they said nothing. They just took a look and avoided eye contact when I turned towards them. I am unsure as to why they reacted like this - frightened of embarrassing me? Perhaps unsure about what to say? In most aspects of life there are so many shades of grey that a generalisation becomes impossible. Not in this case. Here were two groups, one black and one white. Everybody I met fitted neatly into one or the other. That was nice and clear.

There have been plenty of surprises in this campaign and another was the number of people that I would have expected to fall into the 'Dominic group.' Some were simply not up to it. I have some friends who I used to see quite regularly. One of my golfing friends - somebody I played with every weekend for four years, never phoned, he never sent a card or even a text message. On two occasions as I was leaving my gate and crossing the road towards the car park , he was driving past. On seeing me he deemed to slow down and offer a wave. Though my lip reading skills are not well advanced he appeared to shout

'How are you?'

There was no way I could respond as his foot had left the brake pedal and he began to accelerate away. On the second occasion he did this I replied;

'Sod off then you git,' I hoped his lip reading skills were better than mine - Bad Pete.

Another time and about six months into my illness I was walking along the pavement when I met a friend who hadn't contacted me or the family since it had all began. As was her style she made a great fuss of me, a big hug and suddenly became full of questions about us and how we were coping. I nodded in time with her energetic gestures and made the appropriate replies until she said 'You must come round for a coffee.' Without thinking I replied in a straightforward manner, 'No thanks, I don't think I would like that.'

Without a goodbye I returned to my journey and thought briefly about what a nasty person I was. Bad Pete again - I felt the reaction was necessary. The illness through all of its challenges was helping me to see people for what they really were.

Later on a phone call to Dominic gave rise to a conversation which bore no relationship to the exchanges above. We arranged a time to meet later in the afternoon and we started dismantling the shed. After ten minutes a young lad who was no relation to Dominic appeared on his pedal bike and joined our task. I can't even remember his name. He was about twelve years old and was pretty handy with a spanner. In just over an hour the shed was dismantled and ready for removal to my home. That would be another job for another time, I returned home feeling a lot more like my old self. It was a good day.

Chapter 41

Although optimistic about the forthcoming scan I was worried too. Could the condition be in relapse? Would I need to attend more chemotherapy sessions? These were my main concerns. Just a couple of days before the scan I received a phone call from Margaret at work. She invited me in for a cup of tea. I gulped as I considered this - it seemed to be a mammoth task for me to attend work amongst all of this. I decided to accept the invitation as everyone at work had been so thoughtful in their support. I had been keeping the team in touch with my progress through letters and in response, received cards, messages and regular visits in plenty. It was perhaps time to return the favour. I work in two main centres that are about five miles apart in the middle of Leeds. It would not be a wise move to visit one centre without the other so I put a full morning aside in my 'busy schedule' to see how both sets of the team were getting along.

Despite a number of problems they were experiencing at work, they were all sticking to what they do best, helping students with severe disabilities learn more about themselves and the community we live in. The key to this work is collaboration – the ideal being that the many related agencies work together so no one organisation shoulders the full responsibility of such painstaking work. In truth it can be a very isolating experience - so often these students have no status, priority, position or respect from those that plan policy and allocate resources. The students we work alongside usually fall outside the remit of local councils and central government whose priorities lie elsewhere. As a result, teams like mine can feel very alone in the work they carry out. My first visit was to the centre in West Leeds and I managed to arrive as most of the team were turning up for work. They made me feel really welcome and even said I was looking well, which was perhaps an exaggeration.

My hair was coming back now so that is what they must have noticed. We had an hour together during which time they produced a poem they had written to cheer me up. It worked!

My next visit was to our other centre a bit nearer to the middle of Leeds. Here there were another set of greetings that made me feel as if this illness had deprived me of daily contact with friends and colleagues. Margaret had laid on a nice lunch and then a surprise appeared. Each one of the team had brought in a present for me. Each present had been wrapped and dropped into a box that had been decorated by the students. The box was labelled *'For Pete's sake'* and each gift began with the letter 'P.' I managed only to open two of the individual parcels, one contained some Parsley Sauce and the other was a box of Pringles. It would have taken me ages to go open them all.

Work takes a back seat in and amongst an illness like this and I had been very reluctant to go in and see everybody at work. I am pleased that I did. There wasn't much chat about the cancer – I just talked to people who seemed genuinely pleased to see me and gave me the very tangible feeling that I would soon be back at work Two people had to help me out of the building carrying the large box of presents. An hour later I was at home with the children opening the 'P' presents. Gradually I was surrounded by a penguin, a puffin, a bottle of Pinot Grigio, some puzzle books, packets of pepper, poppy and parsley seeds, Polo's, a Pink Panther video, various pens, pickled onions and plenty more. I was still opening presents a week later.

Chapter 42

I mention this episode at work for an important reason. The priority
this year has been getting better of course and work has had to
take a back seat. Despite that it has been a very important part of
my life and will be again. I have had many jobs since my first
paper round. I have collected for Littlewoods football pools as an
evening job while working in a greengrocers during the day. I have
studied for my 'A' level English Literature whilst making Airfix
models in a plastics injection company. I used to make hundreds
of them by day and buy just one of them at the weekend. The
Lancaster bomber remains my favourite. Among all of the models
hanging from the ceiling above my bed, this was somehow the
most reassuring and its presence settled any number of adolescent
problems. I fixed it together with Airfix glue, painted it and then
pinned it to my ceiling suspended on strands of white cotton. It
became hard to turn the light out at night with it hanging over my
head. My mum and dad were very fond of that aeroplane, they
had actually seen it in action during the Second World War. The
plastic Lancaster was just as real for me as I fell asleep underneath
it. I wasn't just some kid trying to get to sleep, I was the rear
gunner hanging upside down in a glass bubble cockpit taking aim
at the enemy. At some point later that night, mum would pop in
and switch out the light.

When I was about sixteen I worked at a garage in a town called
Caterham in Surrey. Most of the time on this job was spent on the
forecourt. A car would pull in and my job was to fill the car up with
petrol. It wasn't at all like the present day experience when you
do all the work yourself only to encounter some surly chap at the
till who can't even be bothered to speak during the transaction.
Back in the seventies the customer didn't move from the driving

seat in his car. I would open the fuel cap and set the petrol pump at automatic. Whilst the fuel pumped into the tank the trick was to nip around the front, open the bonnet and check the oil which always needed a top up. Just a pint of oil was the usual requirement by which time the petrol pump had flicked off. There were some smashing cars; the Ford Anglia vans, the Morris Minor Travellers, a Ford Zephyr, the Hillman Imps, real Mini's and even the Austin Maestro. Occasionally a Japanese motor called a Toyota Corolla would make an appearance. At that time it was even more unusual than the elegant, open topped, hand made, brightly colourerd 'Caterham' cars that would roll through on a regular basis.

On one occasion a Jaguar XJ6 glided in. The owner never moved a muscle, he just barked instructions at me as I checked his tyres. That stunning car had two fuel tanks - one on each side. As the second one was being filled up I nipped into the kiosk to prepare his bill. I had hardly put the carbon paper between the invoice sheets before the owner drove off presuming I had completed all of the jobs on his splendid motor. The first thing I realised was that the petrol pump was still attached to his tank as he drove away. The impact was devastating, the hose was extended to a terrifying tension....the car drove on....the actual petrol pump was ripped from its foundations and the whole left hand wing of the XJ6 imploded. I took the blame and it was time to look for another job.

It must have been nearly thirty or forty minutes before I found one, this time on a building site about four hundred yards away from the garage. At that time I couldn't drive and was riding about on a small Suzuki motorbike. The building site manager decided this experience was enough to warrant my employment as a dumper driver. I agreed with him, at least until I was sat in the dumper. It had three pedals and I only had two feet - what was the other one for? My first job was to deliver two hundred bags of cement to a foundation site at the bottom of a valley. I set off towards the new buildings on my first run. In my dumper were twenty bags of cement and a builder's mate who sat casually on the front of my truck, legs dangling. Only a couple of yards away from a solid brick wall the builder's mate acquired a sixth sense and this sense told him that I didn't know how to stop the dumper. He just about managed to whip his legs away from certain amputation as my dumper ploughed in to the wall destroying twelve feet of breeze block. The outcome was inevitable - sacked from two jobs within a single week and it was only Thursday!

It took nearly the whole of Friday to recover some confidence but by the late afternoon I was on the phone and visiting a couple of pubs to see about bar work. By the following Monday I had somehow stumbled into a dream combination. Between 9.00am and 11.30, I was the gardener in a private block of flats looking after the bushes, lawns, hedges and swimming pool. By noon I had to be at a pub called 'The Commonwealth Arms' to serve customers until 3.00pm and then enjoy a short walk back to the flats to carry on with my gardening job, until the evening. It was perfect:- two more hours to work on my own, listening to the radio and building up a personal relationship with a 'Suffolk Punch' petrol lawn mower.

That was to last six months before the residents association decided to bring in a contract firm to maintain the gardens. By that time I had developed an intimate knowledge of each hedge. I knew how it was shaped, how it grew and where it needed care. I was only given a few hours notice that day and was very upset about losing that job. The second to last thing I did that day was to open the shed and say goodbye to my lawnmower. The very last thing I did was to take most of my clothes off and jump into the pool. I took a deep breath, swam underneath and stuffed my underpants and vest deep into the pumping mechanism. Let the contract firm sort that one out! Another job gone - another one was needed.

That was the pattern - no need for careers advice - just stumbling from one newspaper advert to another. I worked as a butcher for a while - I even made love to one! Worked in a sports shop,a Kentucky Fried Chicken Parlour, I worked as a cleaner in a valve factory and as a kitchen assistant in a private school. I also spent a long time working as a semi-skilled decorator alongside my dad on various building sites across South London. I would marvel at his work rate as he hung up one length of wallpaper after another. To make ends meet dad would have to hang one hundred rolls of wall paper in a week - week after week, month after month. I struggled to keep pace with him as I pasted the lengths of paper and hung them over the top of his step ladder. I was very aware that he had as a young man acquired so many skills in his lengthy apprenticeship. He knew how to grain wood, how to scumble walls, how to design a project from start to finish and see it through with perfection. Yet here he was sweating away on contract work just to keep up the payments. I really couldn't imagine a life like this, it was no life at all.

It was time to make some kind of career - one with prospects. Complete with some 'A' levels I applied to a company called George Wimpey. The job was a 'Commercial Trainee' and it would throw me into the full range of site work including surveys, stores, purchasing, administration and personnel. My first placement was in Mitcham working on a new housing site which was to include the installation of a boating lake. In my first week a row broke out. Of all the builders working on site not many were employed by Wimpey, they were self employed, mostly Irish and with little interest in the welfare of the company. On this particular morning they refused to start work as the canteen was closed and they

163

couldn't get a breakfast. Negotiations rambled on with no success. The union steward shouted at people but there was still no breakfast, still no building. I therefore had no surveying to do so wandered into the office, took the canteen keys opened up the kitchen, turned on the oven and started boiling four dozen eggs. There was a girl called Pauline who did the photocopying and she helped me prepare the bread. Before long we were serving up boiled eggs, mugs of tea and plenty of toast, we even cut the toast into soldiers. The Irish lads liked that touch especially. Breakfast was over and work on site began. Pauline and I became quite popular after that and we were well looked after by the self employed blokes. The shop steward, site manager and office manager were not so sure.

As the year wore on, it was I who became not so sure. The place was riddled with scams and fraud. Lorries would turn up to take 'muck away' from the new boating lake and it was my job to check that each lorry had fifteen square yards of soil and rubble on board before leaving the site. I would climb up, do a rough calculation and then issue a docket to the driver which would be proof of his work and approve payment for him. Before long lorries were attempting to leave the site empty and I would be offered cash for the issue of a docket. The site manager who was employed by George Wimpey told me to make sure I didn't succomb to this scam and to keep a tight rein on these dodgy deals. One morning I came into work really early and spotted him and the office manager signing dockets by the handful and receiving cash for each one. Not a lorry in sight.

One week when working in the store, I took delivery and signed for sixty kitchens even though the building site was still at a foundation stage. By the following Monday each and every single box of cupboards, ovens, hobs, fridges and cabinets had gone from the delivery area. They had disappeared over the weekend and I was told to ask no questions nor make any fuss. I travelled to the Head Office in Hammersmith, spilled the beans and resigned.

My Dad was still hanging a hundred rolls of wallpaper a week and the bottom of his step ladder seemed a more honest place to be than to choose a salaried career of conspiracy and fraud. I don't suppose that company was any worse than any other building company. Despite their cheating George Wimpey and all of the other companies thrived throughout the eighties and the nineties. I for one was not sorry to hear of the mess these companies had landed themselves in by the credit crunch of 2009. It was about time.

Chapter 43

Out of necessity I was ready to take any job that would help pay my rent and pay my bills and at last I struck lucky, though at first I had no idea that this job would shape the rest of my working life. I took on a job as a nursing assistant in a hospital for the 'mentally handicapped' as it was called then. It was a huge place with fifteen hundred residents, the youngest lived on a children's ward along with forty other kids. He was only three years old. The oldest lived on a different corridor in a ward with thirty other elderly ladies. She was just over one hundred years old. Those in between included people with severe learning difficulties, physical disabilities or a combination of both. Many had such a severe medical condition that learning opportunities could never have made any real impact. The large Victorian building was hidden from the outside community by huge conifer trees which made it very difficult to gain a view even if you were passing on the top of a double decker bus. As a child, I remember seeing the residents hanging around by the iron gate as they stood smoking and looking out on a community that preferred to think this place didn't exist. The residents stood there for most of the day as if waiting for something to happen, same people, same pose, same outlook.

In my brief visit before the interview I was shown the building from the inside. It was mostly designed to resemble the shape of the letter 'H' with a connecting corridor between the male and female sides. Each of the main corridors I would estimate to be four hundred yards long but they looked longer with a tiny light blinking in the distance as the exit door closed and opened. The corridors were full of people as they carried out their business moving slowly from their wards towards a day service or a day activity. The poor lighting available just revealed these characters as silhouettes of all shapes and sizes, most were walking, some were lying on the floor, a few stood still flicking a piece of string. There were seven blocks of buildings attached to each side of the hospital. These were labelled 'A' to 'G' and each block had three floors. On each one of these floors was a ward and on each ward lived about forty people. The residents of each ward spent the day time hours in a large recreation room and went to bed at night in a slightly bigger room containing forty beds and not even a curtain to offer any privacy.

As my visit progressed I was shown quickly around some of the departments and vocational areas. There was a gardening section with greenhouses and sheds, a tinsmith, a cobblers shop and a laundry. There was also a large portacabin with about two hundred people inside. They were assembling hundreds of catering packages on contract work for British Airways. Since that visit I have never been able to unfold a small catering pack of knife fork and serviette without thinking of this place. As our small group progressed we were shown a children's school complete with teachers and a headmaster, an Art Therapy room, an adventure playground with three rabbits and a lively music room. It was a confusing mixture. There were the facilities needed to keep such an institution operating efficiently alongside the presence of more modern and therapeutic services that had been shoe horned into this place over the last twenty years. For someone who had only previously seen the Victorian chimneys belonging to this hospital from the top of a bus, it was quite a surprise. In short, it was a town within a town.

Within a couple of weeks I had arrived for my new job which was on MC1. Male Corridor, in Block C and on the 1st floor. There were forty residents, nearly thirty of whom used a wheelchair. The men were aged fifty years and above. The dozen or so members of this ward who were able to walk helped the nurses care for those who couldn't as part of their activities. On each shift there were three or four nurses including a Charge Nurse, a Staff Nurse and a couple of people like me just there as a nursing assistant. It must have been obvious to the Charge Nurse that I was a brand new member of staff due to the voluminous shining white coat I was hiding beneath. It was 7am.

'First job' he instructed 'Go to the store cupboard, get some cleaning kit and go and clean Bill up. You will find him in the bathroom.'

Thinking Bill had probably spilled some tea on himself or needing help brushing his teeth I pulled out a towel and flannel from the cupboard, a new tooth brush and some toothpaste. I found my way to the bathroom. It was huge with four cast iron baths standing tall on claw feet. Each bath had an oval shaped piece of wood made from solid hardwood planks. Lying on the top of one of these boards was Bill. He was clenched up in a ball, naked and covered in faeces which he was eating just as fast as he was producing it. I looked at my flannel and toothbrush they seemed rather lightweight for the job, they looked back at me and told each other that I was inadequate too. Over the next eight hours the range of jobs made working for George Wimpey look easier than the easiest job in Easy Town. After Bill had finished his 'meal' my duty was to operate a wall mounted industrial shaving machine and by breakfast time I had given the thirty men who used wheelchairs an electric shave as they were pushed one by one to the front of this long queue. Many of these men could have shaved themselves, I was sure of it, but this was the routine and it was not the time to suggest any other method. By the time my shift finished that afternoon I felt as if I would never be able to eat another thing. Some of the jobs and the way they were allocated to fulfil the needs of these poor men were inhuman. I was convinced that I couldn't turn up for work on my second day but I did just as I did on the third day and then the fourth.

The rest is a personal history. It isn't a history of great achievement or celebrity status, nor of achieving the unachievable. I couldn't pretend that I have overcome insurmountable barriers or even done anything remotely newsworthy. At the age of fifty three I can at least look back on thirty years that have provided real meaning to my working life, a huge array of satisfaction and a career that has been shared with so many like minded people. That is something not everyone can say. I feel certain that had I remained in the commercial building industry these values would not have been experienced or enjoyed - I might have been richer though.

Despite that, my career is important to me especially as it includes working alongside people with severe disabilities and the daily surprises that this brings. All that has to be postponed for now, my job at the moment is to get better, I have no other job no other goal. When that is achieved I can rejoin Margaret, Aileen, Jennie, Kathy and the rest of my team in Leeds to carry on as before, most likely with a different viewpoint. The Hodgkin's Lymphoma has seen to that.

Chapter 44

At last the long wait in 'no mans land' came to an end and the day arrived to attend my local hospital for the scan. This event seemed to have great significance to my friends and family and the phone calls increased in number prior to the scan and for a long time afterwards. I hadn't really understood the implications of the last scan I had undergone, but I forced myself to remember that it had been a positive result. The symptoms experienced last summer had all gone. The weight loss, the high temperatures, the fatigue and most of all those awful night sweats had disappeared. The chemotherapy, the necessary evil was solely responsible for any problems I was now experiencing. The toxins were working their way around and out of my body.

Physically I had a painful itch all around my waist. My back, knee and ankle joints felt arthritic. Emotionally I was still dreaming about Captain Chemo, still waking up in a panic believing I was back in the side room and still suffering from the associations that heightened my sense of smell and the subsequent reactions. It was really helpful to be visiting the hospice for the art group and my Reiki. By now I was halfway through a painting of a french market scene. At the hospice I could talk about my fears to people who had been through similar experiences and had survived. Another thing, I was no longer the newest member of this day service and I could talk to people who were just at the beginning of their treatment regime. This was all part of the recovery process and it felt important to be there just painting and talking and be seen as a piece of real life evidence to prove that the chemotherapy would eventually come to an end.

However I was now back in the clinical world and sat in a waiting room preparing for the scan. At my last CT scan I had been asked to undress straight away, I had sat for nearly an hour waiting with three ladies. The room was really cold and I had to ask for a blanket for the oldest of the women. She was shivering and seemed very frightened about what may follow. I did my best to reassure her about the procedure. There was no real need for her to have been so scared and I am sure one of the staff could have eased her worries with a brief chat, but it didn't happen. We were all wearing one of those gowns that fasten up at the back and sitting in our chairs with our socks on drinking a couple of pints of juice that tasted like aniseed. By the time my appointment arrived I was busting for a wee. The elderly lady wrapped in the blanket was having a much harder time of this than I was.

The system this time seemed more dignified as if somebody had actually thought about easing the humiliation just a tiny bit. I wasn't requested to undress straight away, as I had been before, and the room was nice and warm. I was told how much time I had to drink my aniseed juice and informed that I would be called a little nearer the time. Just five minutes before my scan was due I was asked to undress in a changing room, put on the gown and keep on my pants and socks. It was only then I took up my place in the waiting room again and spoke to another nervous lady called Susan who was about to undertake her first scan. She was very concerned about the procedure to come and was in real discomfort as she needed the loo desperately. I was prepared to let her go in first but thought I had better not mess the system up. The staff there work on lists and I didn't want Susan to go into the room in my place only to be scanned for Hodgkin's Lymphoma. As we talked I was called into the nurses room for the observations on my blood pressure and from there ushered into the scanner room. The CT scan room is clean and clinical and two staff wait there as if they are to strap you into a guillotine. Unlike the PET scan the machine is not as deep and looks like a huge polo mint. I would be on a narrow bed that would move in and out of a hole. The nurses were quiet and efficient and I remember thinking that their cool manner was going to scare Susan senseless when she came in. No problem for me though - by now I was an expert. This was my fifth scan. The only real discomfort is the dye that is injected into your arm. That is never particularly nice though nowhere near as bad as the feeling you get about two minutes later - my testicles heated up and continued to get even hotter. I had forgotten about this unpleasant experience probably out of necessity and I was glad that I hadn't been sat in the waiting room worrying about it happening again. Just as if it felt both testicles were to lift six inches above my body and explode, they cooled down again and I settled in for the instructions that were to follow.

By now the nurses had retreated to the safety of their protected room and a emotionally stagnant voice gave me strict instructions via a loudspeaker. It wasn't very nice really, I am sure extra efforts could be made to ease the anxiety especially for people going through it for the first time. If the voice in the loudspeaker could be a bit more human that would help tremendously. I don't mean the nurse should say something like, 'I bet your balls have never felt so big' , no scan result would be very helpful if the patient's body was moving around in laughter - but just a touch of humanity wouldn't go amiss. Ten minutes later I was off the bed, away from the polo mint and back in the waiting room. Susan had disappeared and by now was probably taking my place at the scanner, at least her testicles wouldn't be a problem.

Chapter 45

I had about a week to wait for the results and these would be delivered by my usual consultant at Pontefract Hospital. Kate and I both attended the appointment with him at the clinic. As usual we were late going in, but this time over an hour late. By then the phone had ganged up with the usual number of text messages from near and far, each message enquiring about the outcome. Yet again I was in no position to reply, I had to wait a bit longer and demonstrate more patience. We were called to Dr. Wright's room and he confirmed that as expected the scan had revealed no cancerous activity was going on. He would define me as 'in remission.' My memory spun back to the time when he delivered my diagnosis in the room with brown leather seats.

'Our aim is to get you into remission' he had stated.

That is what he had done. The news was quickly delivered and low key, there was no celebration and the process wasn't over, I would be back to see him for a number of years and the next appointment would be in three months. I had hoped for this news and had been expecting it. It was still great to hear though and I had already prepared a short sentence or two to thank him and the team for all they had done for me. I preferred to do it this way rather than rely on impulse. I am sure the emotion of the occasion would have overcome me if I had been relying on something spontaneous. We left the clinic, crossed the road and visited the nurses on the Dr. Jackson ward. I wasn't prepared for this however and just stood there as Kate spoke to them all. She said all that I could have ever wanted to say and did it more eloquently than I could have done. With that we were gone from this busy place and I walked slowly and calmly along the corridor to the exit door.

It was only a short walk but one that had seemed like a half marathon on so many previous occasions. We sat in the car, hugged each other and set off home. As Kate drove I struggled with my mobile phone and tried to reply to the dozen messages that were keenly bleeping away. The news was on the radio, Fred Goodwin was refusing to give some of his pension back to the taxpayers. Then the sport came on, Middlesbrough were deep in relegation trouble having just lost to Newcastle. I pressed a button and retuned the station - a song came on, somebody called Lily Allen was performing, it was nice little tune called 'The Fear.' It was just an ordinary song, it passed the time away, it had no deep significance, it was just an ordinary day.... at last.

The invasion, the occupation and the ceasefire within my tiny empire were over. On the way home we stopped at the local shop and I bought a bottle of Cava to celebrate the news. I couldn't afford Champagne. As I paid for this I knew that I wouldn't be opening it just yet. The magic word 'cure' hadn't been mentioned and it couldn't be. Remission is, for the foreseeable future, as good as it will get. I would be monitored on a regular basis and would need to return to the hospital if any of the symptoms came back. The fear of a relapse, however unlikely, would be present for a long time to come. So it was that I entered the house, strangely subdued, the phone already ringing. I felt very guilty that I didn't feel like clicking my heels. After all, I had met so many people over the last year who would have given anything to swap places with me. I felt very disloyal to them especially to the few who hadn't pulled through. The reactions from all my supporters, friends and family were to be ecstatic over the next few days and very welcome, at least on the face of it. By then the cards started appearing through the post, most of them depicting a bottle of champagne with a cork flying through the air. My bottle of cheap Cava stayed in the boot of the car.

"Truce"

Chapter 46

I knew I was entering a new phase in this battle and found it very difficult to come to terms with. My buddy Russell was on hand again as I telephoned him for help. It was a great relief to find that he had felt exactly the same while all around him were celebrating. The illness remained it wasn't cured, just in abeyance. His advice was to look forward and just try to get on with my life. My challenge now was to bring back the kind of lifestyle that I felt happy with. As usual this was helped along by the kids. Michael had a friend over for tea, her name was Emily. They didn't know I could hear them chatting

'Your Dad has got more hair now.' She remarked casually.
'Yeah - his Hodgkins is getting better. Someone told me it would only take three months but it has been longer.' Michael replied.
She considered this for a moment, looked at Minnie and said
'Your dog has a lot of hair.'

There we had it, the kids were thinking it was nearly over and it was time for me to do the same. There should be a sense of normality creeping back into our lives and it was Michael, Joe and Kate that deserved this the most. Going back to work was still a long way off, my doctor had given me a sick note for another two months. From an emotional point of view I was pleased to be given this time. From a financial point of view this wasn't such good news. My wages had just about run out, the employer had given me four months full pay and four months on half. This was a good deal really but I soon found myself dipping into the savings we had made over the last couple of years. These savings had been earmarked for a new central heating boiler. The situation meant we had to use this money to keep everything going with the exception of a reliable central heating system. Like many of us I had never been one for taking out extra insurances. The ones you must have seem bad enough, car, house, contents, mortgage, buildings, the endless and familiar annual list. The opportunity of protecting car loans and the mortgage against critical illness had been overlooked. I of course regretted this now though in comparison to the prospect of losing my life I shouldn't regret it too much.

As my wages ran out I had to apply for a new benefit called Employment Support Allowance. This was a new experience for me for even as a school leaver in between jobs I had never 'signed on' before. Whenever I needed money I just found another job that would pay me a few quid. The application process for this benefit was of one of the most humiliating experiences that I had encountered to date. Firstly it was so difficult finding the right office that would begin my claim, I would spend ages talking to robotic machines on my telephone only to be given the same phone number that I had rung in the first instance. Eventually I was able to book an appointment on the telephone to lodge a claim. The phone call took one and a half hours. The problem seemed to be that I wasn't actually looking for work, I had a job to go back to, but was just off sick. This didn't quite sit well with the computer programme that was attending to my needs.

A few weeks later the whole telephone conversation was sent to me by post and I had to go through it all again, make any amendments and send in a huge number of documents. It was harder than being at work! My bank is the one that spends thousands of pounds filming one of their office workers singing very badly while riding a surf board. I sometimes received the benefits of this multi million advertising campaign as a credit in my current account. Despite the promises Howard made about getting fifty times more interest than any other bank, the most I have ever had in interest is thirty four pence. Even this pitiful amount had to be certificated for the purposes of this gaining this Employment Support Allowance. Eventually the claim was complete.

It still wasn't over; I had to complain four weeks later that I had received no money and again four weeks after that. It took the individual efforts of a very kindly lady to extract some money from the Department of Work and Pensions and she sorted out a Giro cheque for me. I was now in receipt of £64.50 per week. A week later I received a letter saying that my income had been reassessed and my benefit was to reduce by four pounds. I bet the thirty four pence 'Halifax Howard' gave to me was to blame. As I mentioned this was the first time I had claimed benefit and I did so knowing that I would be returning to work eventually. This made the prospect of such a low income less threatening. Imagine however if you were relying on this kind of support for a long period of time - it must be nigh on impossible. The other thought that occurred to me during this process related to people who are not very good on the phone, not very good at paperwork and not very good at complaining. How do they cope?

Chapter 47

Our first trip away came along in the form of a weekend in Whitby with our friends Michelle, Chad and their son Mathew. Until now, we had been staying within reach of the hospital in case I contracted a high temperature. It had been nine months since our trip to Pagham beach in Sussex when the holiday was abandoned and we came home. The Whitby trip was to be a short one but I was looking forward to it so much. All looked well, the weather was good, the packing was done and everybody was fit. Nothing could spoil this - surely. When we came downstairs on the departure morning we discovered Minnie, she was really poorly and very sick. Any chance of driving off was postponed as the vet's appointment was booked. In the end I took the children to Whitby and Kate remained at home for another night. She joined us the next day with a much recovered dog. The remainder of the weekend went well enjoying a good time with good friends. I felt well looked after and enjoyed a game of football on the beach, the traditional pitch and putt and all of the other games we made up between us. This is what Russell my buddy had meant when he advised me to get on with life and enjoy it.

My illness had postponed a job that I had needed to do in Whitby. The Abbey overlooking the town was my Dad's favourite place and Mum wanted some of his ashes spreading up there. I set off early on the Sunday morning before anybody else was awake and drove into the old part of the town. I parked the car and found my way through the quiet streets to the bottom to the famous 199 steps. We had climbed them so often as kids, counting each one as we went as if checking that one hadn't been removed since our last visit. On this particular morning I didn't have the enthusiastic legs of a nine year old, nor did I count the steps. They were incredibly steep and difficult to climb.

I was shocked at how hard I found them to ascend. At least four times I had to rest, sit on a step and look back across the harbour, waiting for my energy to return. Eventually I reached the summit-it must have been years since I was last there and at the top of the steps I discovered an access road and car park! Then another surprise; the Abbey itself was all locked up with iron gates and impossible to access early on a morning. That actually solved a problem for me - I had been worried about spreading his ashes around the abbey in such an informal way.... there probably was some bureaucratic procedure that I should have gone through with the County Council before I even embarked on such a plan. To solve this problem I had devised a cunning plan; I had put on a pair of trousers with a hole in the pocket. Once in position I had planned to break the bag with my Dad's ashes in it and spread them discretely through my trouser leg as I walked about.

I gained the idea from a Steve McQueen film. The Great Escape was one of my Dad's favourite movies and it would be just like the scene when the prisoners were smuggling the earth away from their escape tunnel by dropping it through their trouser pockets into the outdoor compound. There was no need for such deception, I couldn't get in to the Abbey. It didn't matter at all, I was quite pleased, I had never really wanted to say goodbye to my Dad as he slid past the right leg of my boxer shorts. I spotted an imposing Celtic Cross on the headland just next to the Abbey, overlooking the town of Whitby. It was there that I spread his ashes... we had a chat about old times... shared a short prayer... said goodbye. I then turned away and found my way back down the steps. I stopped again on the way down a couple of times not because I was tired, it was to think a bit longer about him and my Mum. I then thought about Kate and the children, my illness and what lay ahead for us. It compared well to the quiet town in front of me and the North Yorkshire Moors beyond. It was a grand view and a

179

grand outlook. Happy with all of this I skipped down the last fifty steps and found my way back to my family and friends. When I arrived back at the cottage it was still early in the morning and not even the children had stirred.

Chapter 48

This trip away to the seaside had been a huge step towards the life I had occupied before the invasion. Even jobs that needed doing at home were all an integral part of this peaceful time. The shed was finished off with some more help from Dominic, our allotment though a touch haphazard in comparison to surrounding plots looked in decent shape and I slowly built a chicken run using some wood that I had found in a nearby skip. I visited a battery farm and bought three chickens to go in it. Their expression was one of bewilderment as they postured and positioned themselves in the new run, pecking at berries and fresh weeds. I actually felt some empathy with these birds. It was good to be let out! When I think of someone like Lance Armstrong who recovered from cancer and went on to win six 'Tours De France,' – not one of my events could be listed as any great achievement. Shifting a shed can hardly be compared with the punishing climbs that he conquered on a racing bike through the French Alps. I felt as if I had climbed my mountain by turning up for those last four treatments in hospital. These subsequent weeks felt like I was over the summit and freewheeling down the hill on the other side.

That of course is exactly the time when something can hit you hard ...really hard! I imagined enjoying a bicycle ride, relaxing and looking around at the view just as a piece of discarded metal tent pole flicked up and lodged itself right in the middle of my spokes. The ensuing crash made worse mostly due to the surprise of such an incident. In fact I felt prepared for something to go wrong and had good reason. In 1995 I had reached a point when all the troubles of looking after two kids as a single parent had begun to settle down. It wasn't exactly freewheeling, but neither was I pedaling like a lunatic. Sam and Rosie had settled into their new school, the small house we lived in looked like a home and I had some systems in place that kept me going. Each night once the children were in bed I would pour a small whisky, open up my bureau, light a candle and write a few pages about the experience of losing their mum. It helped me cope in two ways. Firstly to try and make sense of the problems encountered in that fateful eleventh year of our marriage and secondly to help manage the fortnightly visits that the children made to Scarborough. It was still very traumatic.

After a few pages of writing I would clear up any mess and set the table ready for the morning with a full set of white crockery that I had bought from British Home Stores. It was a ritual I had then and not one that I still indulge in. At the time it felt important to have this kind of order, the cups, saucers, bowls, dishes, plates, teapot and eggcups all lined up and waiting. They even matched the lyncrusta wallpaper on the kitchen walls! This was a coincidence by the way - I am not that sad. I was pleased with the ordered scene as I switched out the kitchen light and went up to bed. In the morning it was all still there and as usual we hardly used any of it - just the cereal bowls and sometimes an egg cup.

Another positive in all of this, which was no coincidence, was the relationship I had built up with Kate. She would visit us once or twice a week from her home in Leeds with her dog, Leah and we looked forward to them turning up. She would help with the children's school uniforms by sewing in name labels, she would take Sam and Rosie to the park, help with their bits of homework and at night time she would read them the Myths and Legends. I first met her at work in a college a few years before my wife and I split up. I liked her a lot. When the rock star intervened in my marriage it felt natural enough to develop the friendship with Kate but that was all too easy. Of all the friends and of all the different advice they offered me it was Kate who made the most sense; 'Your job is to forget whatever we could have together and get back to your wife, sort everything out as best you can. Talk, talk and talk some more. It is the only choice you have.'

I followed this sound advice beyond anything else and stuck to it for as long as I could before having to give up the idea that my wife and I would ever regain a stable and secure home for the Sam and Rosie. I probably didn't fully give up until my wife asked me to grant her a divorce on the grounds of adultery and I agreed. She would become my ex-wife. I now found myself setting up a 'good enough' home and was very pleased with the progress made. I asked Kate to move in with us and she agreed to do so. It was a big commitment as she was starting a relationship not just with me but with two children as well, now aged seven and six. That is when that discarded bit of tent pole flicked up and lodged in my spokes. All the progress made cycling up that mountain pass came to a crashing end and my face ended up scraping painfully along the gravel.

Early one evening about two hours before the children went to bed, three hours before I opened up my writing bureau and four hours before I set up my British Home Stores breakfast collection - a knock came at the door. I didn't know if a 'helpful' friend had made contact with my ex-wife or if Sam or Rosie had leaked the fact that Kate was moving in to our home, but here she was at the door. She had left the rock star, driven down from Scarborough and was stood on my doorstep. Without coming in she just said;

'I have made a big mistake, I want to be the kids' mum again , I want to be back with the three of you.'

Due to the shock I don't remember anything else she said in the short time she was in the house. I made some tea and wiped the kitchen tops over and over again as she tearfully sipped her drink. When the kitchen tops were clean I started cleaning the grill of the oven. I couldn't sit down and discuss much with her- I didn't know how to, so took refuge in a 'J' cloth. That gave me some thinking time and before long we decided she should leave and visit a mutual friend who lived close by. I think she stayed the night there. Whatever the circumstances that night, my bureau was never opened nor was my breakfast set laid out, I am sure I didn't forget the drink of whisky. The very event I had strived to achieve two years earlier was now happening right in front of me. This was to be the hardest decision of my life. It felt exactly as if my little face was scraping along the loose gravel of a road, the decision whatever way it went was to be so painful. The choice was clear enough - should I take her back or continue with the new life that I had built with my girlfriend Kate. A simple enough problem but the elements of it were deep and complex.

The next few weeks were so difficult for everybody. I couldn't take her back and Kate moved in as planned. Until the kids mum had turned up on the doorstep I felt as if I had done all I could to safeguard the children's happiness and security. By not restoring her to her natural role I was now the main reason that Sam and Rosie were not going to live with their real mum. On the other hand Kate had helped us so much over the last two years. Those weekly visits had kept my heart and soul together and given me strength in situations that I would have otherwise found impossible. The decision weighed heavily upon me and three weeks after Kate had moved in I asked her to move out again. It was a very cruel thing to do and I looking back I am ashamed of it. The only defence that I can muster for myself was the devastating confusion that I was experiencing following the visit from Scarborough.

Despite the treatment I had inflicted on Kate for some reason she 'hung in' and continued to support the three of us from afar. There

184

were a couple of occasions that gave me some clarity and helped me realise what a fool I had been. I had been delayed at work for something vaguely important and I was under pressure to get home and meet the children from school. Kate, who knew I was under pressure, drove up to the school and made sure Sam and Rosie were safe, she took them home, gave them some tea and left when I arrived home.

The second event involved a trip I made to Scarborough to collect Sam and Rosie. It was a very stormy Sunday evening when I collected them. I was driving a ridiculous Fiat campervan at the time and it was notoriously unreliable. As we set off for Wakefield the sky darkened and a terrible storm took its toll on the van. It stuttered and shuddered along until I took shelter in a petrol station. The storm worsened with fork lightening all around. There was a nearby strike and the electric lights in the petrol station and in the nearby village all went out. So did our chances of getting any petrol. We eventually limped home at 11pm. It had taken six hours to get home and I was fretting about the Sunday night jobs that were still to be carried out. As I pulled up outside of our house I noticed the lights were on. Kate had somehow figured out I was struggling to get home. As the three of us came in I discovered Kate had let herself in, prepared the kids school uniforms and packed their lunches for the next day. She even had some supper ready and had laid out my BHS breakfast set! These two incidents gave me a good slapping on both cheeks and the impact told me what I had known all along.... I was lucky to still have this help, I was amazed that Kate had decided to keep in touch with us despite all I had done to her. Nothing again would make me doubt our future together. I asked her to move back in and I couldn't believe my good fortune when she agreed.

Chapter 49

I was grateful that my recovery from Hodgkin's Lymphoma had not undergone such a shock to the system. No unexpected visitor had knocked on my door and no impossible decisons had to be reached. My joints and emotions were suffering. Either of these were likely to break down at any time. I found it difficult to walk with any reliable stability for an hour or two in the morning and for half an hour after I rose from a chair. When I sat and thought about the previous six months I felt overwhelmed for many reasons, none of which needed explanation. Life was slowly returning to normal. As normal, Thornes Juniors third team were still losing each week. A rather pleasant bond had been formed between the group of parents that turned up each week to see the team lose again. It was the last game of the season. So far the results read: played 25... won 0... lost 24 and drawn 1. The final game was against Nostell at a very plush football centre in Crofton. The support for the lads was noticeably more vocal than usual as if we all needed a good result to end the season. I really hoped so for the lads sake but I also had something in my bag that I wouldn't be able to reveal if were to lose yet again.

The game was competitive enough and we didn't concede too many. With just five minutes left we were only two goals down and we parents were still urging the team on. Two minutes later we scored, a nice goal too. Joe scrambled a ball in from the left and there was young George to thump it into the net. The referee was about to blow the full time whistle when exactly the same move happened. Another goal from George. It was two each! Then the whistle did go. After a season of defeats.... over 100 conceded goals.... tears and disappointment, the lads had managed just their second point of the season. They were as delighted as you could imagine and so were the parents. As the team's coach sat the lads down and tried to express his delight, I put my hand in my bag. At last! It was the bottle of Cava that I had bought when Dr. Wright gave me the news about my remission. As the lads received their final team talk of the season I shook the bottle, popped the cork and sprayed it all over the team in good 'Formula One' style. That was another good day. They were adding up.

Chapter 50

With the experience of a successful weekend away in Whitby to look back upon, it was with some shared confidence that we set off on our holiday to Holy Island. Preparations went quite well though we set off nearer noon than the planned 10am. Only five minutes into the journey and just before the motorway we turned back home for the directions and details that we needed to find our cottage. As we parked outside our house, Pat our neighbour waved at us from her window. She keeps an eye out for us when we go on holiday. Rarely do we set off without having to come back five minutes later, this was no exception.

We set off again waving to Pat, as is the custom, and this time there was no turning back. It was a very hot Saturday morning at the end of May. One of the reasons for being on time was to settle into our holiday home in time for the F.A. Cup Final. Joe and I were keenest on this of course, Michael and Kate just wanted to get there safely. Three hours later we had travelled the one hundred and eighty miles to Holy Island and were driving across the causeway at low tide. My keenness to see the start of the final distracted me from the scenery that lay ahead which was a shame. The island was just as I remembered it from my day trip years earlier, busy with day trippers and the car park outside of the village looked full. At five minutes to three we had abandoned the car, the bikes, all of the luggage and bags of groceries outside the cottage. We were to stay there for the full week. Joe and I were standing in front of the television which looked fairly new though the video player connected to it suggested the set was about twenty years old. Horror! As the tv warmed up, only the sound came on. We listened to the national anthem being sung at Wembley and urgently shouted for Michael to come and fix our problem. He was upstairs exploring the cottage with Kate and in response calmly walked down the stairs before methodically going through each of the eighty potential channels looking for visual reception.

The match had started and still no picture. Just twenty five seconds into the game, Everton scored the fastest ever goal in an F.A. Cup final. As a Middlesbrough fan I remember Roberto De Mateo scoring for Chelsea inside forty seconds at the 1995 final, but this was quicker than that and we had missed it. Michael eliminated one problem after another before turning his attention to a recently installed DVD player which was showing a green light. He pressed a button the light changed to red and there was the picture - a steaming hot Wembley and only eight minutes into the match. Fifteen minutes later I was untangling the kids bikes from the bike rack and Joe popped his head out of the door, 'Drogba has equalised' he squealed. Another missed goal.

With jobs to do as we settled into the cottage I kept one eye on the television and helped Kate unpack the cases. With this all done I made us a well deserved cup of tea. There were still twenty minutes of the match left. It became a unique final for me, I achieved a hat trick of missed goals. Frank Lampard scored as I was squeezing out the last tea bag. All three goals missed. I did see a great goal towards the end of the match but the officials believed that Milouda's shot didn't cross the line as it bounced down off the cross bar - a great goal, but disallowed.

I was quite pleased when the final was over, the tension of it was out of kilter with the calmness enveloping this island. It was time to relax and forget about anything too exciting. A short walk with Minnie around the village revealed a scurry of last minute visitors racing to the causeway in order to escape the high tide. Within twenty minutes the island had become quiet, peaceful and inhabited only by one hundred and forty villagers and the 'outsiders', such as ourselves, who were staying in a rented cottage.

My hunch that the island would transform into a serene and mystical place was correct. This would be a great place to recharge our batteries and to rebuild our boundaries. It had been a hard year for us all, especially Kate. I was worried that since I had been feeling stronger, she had appeared weaker. Kate had been holding on to this family for the last ten months, there had been so much to do, especially at times when I was too ill to help. I hoped the week away would help her regain some energy.

Chapter 51

We were awakened the next morning at 4am by the sun as it popped up over Lindisfarne Castle and lit up the whole of our bedroom through the thin cream curtains. The lads were also up so I joined them and breakfast was over before 5am. Our cottage looked right over the castle which looked to be no more than a mile away and the scene inspired me to start some exercise. I used to be a decent runner, nothing too fast, but in my twenties and thirties I ran about twenty half marathons. I also managed one full marathon in the time of three hours and forty five minutes at Scarborough. I remember feeling quite pleased with myself until I was overtaken in the last mile by an ageing Jimmy Saville. I stared at the winding road leading to the castle and thought '*How about that then.*'

I felt a little nervous as I put on my shorts and trainers, it was a glorious day and already quite hot outside as Minnie and I considered the run to the castle. My clicking and aching joints seemed very surprised as we set off and repaid me with a lack of co-operation. My legs felt as if they belonged to the late Charles Hawtry. He was the skinny chaotic one with round rimmed glasses in the Carry On films. My legs were moving but didn't feel connected to my willing spirit. Minnie sped on ahead of me with an occasional glance backwards showing me how it should be done. My feet were beating on the tarmac making a loud flat-footed slap as I progressed up the hill. It was a jog that bore no similarity to my pre-chemotherapy abilities. It was awful. I kept going in best 'carry on' style and despite the slight gradient managed to reach the castle. There was a bench that I had my eye on but that joy was to be postponed slightly. A sheep had somehow broken through its fencing and was trying to get back to its chums in the field. Minnie responded to my urgent shout and sat down while I managed to push the lost ewe back through a gap in the stile. Then I sat down - the view from the castle was beautiful, the sea was calm, the village bathed in the bright morning sunshine and a fishing boat was returning to the small jetty on the other side of the bay. It couldn't have been better, it really couldn't.

On the path meandering down from the castle, a figure appeared. We exchanged greetings and set off walking back to the village together. He was a retired fisherman who was born on the island. He had spent his entire career as a crew member on the local boats, working from the small jetty, catching crab and lobster. It was a pleasant walk with him as we talked about his birthplace. I learned how the island desperately needed the tourists to give the dwindling number of villagers a livelihood - yet the tide gave this quiet island back to the local people twice a day. This seemed like an ideal arrangement, the lack of burger bars, penny arcades and chip shops were testament to it. We talked a bit longer and soon reached the village. His journey to work had been a three minute walk from the gate at his back garden to the fishing jetty for a total of forty five years. Even then he had been late sometimes! I couldn't help but compare this to my own journey along the M621 to Leeds which normally takes one hour to cover fourteen miles. There must be some disadvantage to living here with a life ruled by the tide? As the walk neared its end I was struggling to think of any problems that living here would create. As we parted, probably to meet on another morning a disadvantage did occur to me; imagine living here and having to visit the hospital urgently with a temperature of forty degrees. At high tide the curlews, herons, arctic terns, the sunrise and the constant mystery of the place may not look quite so convenient or pleasurable.

Chapter 52

The next morning, if possible, seemed even sunnier than the one before as I set off on my run to the castle. This time my legs co-operated with me to a much greater extent and I arrived at the resting bench fairly quickly. It felt great to be running again, even for this short distance. Breakfast had been a little later today thanks to the black bin bags we had hung over the thin cream curtains. (An experienced parent's trick). Exploring the island was the main challenge of the day. Kate and Michael set off on their bikes while Joe and I spent some time in the village. It was a quiet time so a good chance to help him gain some confidence on his bike before the traffic rolled in at the change of tide. After a while we set off in the direction that Michael and Kate had taken with Joe pedalling on ahead. Half an hour later we were well away from the village and I was enjoying a bare foot walk through the warm waters of a receding tide and enjoying the views that were all around me. No relaxing music or tapes of whales or waterfalls could match this. As I sunk deeper into this sensation Joe disappeared amongst the sea grass up ahead. At that moment Michael and Kate appeared around the headland pushing their bikes. Minnie spotted the pair and flew off to meet them. A single car appeared heading towards the village, the timing was unlucky, Minnie escaped being run over by a hair's breadth. Michael had taken a bad tumble from his bike and seemed very upset, the near fatality to his dog he had witnessed didn't help much. Joe meanwhile appeared in the distance. On reaching him the gears and chain on his bike were choked with seaweed and he had mud up to his knees. Family life, nothing like it!

We all limped back to our new home still intact but only just. The afternoon proved eventful too. The plan was to spend the afternoon on Bamburgh beach while the weather remained so hot. Once all the bits for the trip had been gathered we sat in the car to set off. The ignition didn't respond - the battery was flat. One of the children had left the interior light on and now we were stumped. The roads are mostly flat here so jump needs would be needed. Everyone piled back out of the car and I set off to the village in search of some jump leads. I had only walked twenty yards before I met tall man with long hair, a beard and a bandana. There was something familiar about him,

'Jamie, is that you?' I enquired.
'Yes it is, how are you?' he responded.

Here we are, miles from home in a bit of trouble and I bump into someone who used to live over the road from me. In truth, as neighbours, it had been a slightly uncomfortable relationship. There had been some trouble between his teenage sons who had upset Pat and Dave. We never really understood where we were with Jamie's family, they were acquaintances more than friends. We all shared a car park which I think had been part of the problem.

I recall driving home from work when they lived near us and parking up. There were three reasons for remaining seated in my car, I was listening to an interview on the radio, I was eating an apple and I saw Jamie trying to fix a wheel on his camper van. He was struggling with it and my first thought was to go and give him a hand. I resisted this as some fun could be had here. It was 'bad Pete' again. He was getting nowhere with his wheel brace and eventually decided to put his full wait upon it. It bent right over and I watched his lips form the expected curse before ripping the now useless brace away from the wheel nuts and throwing it in a bush. He then started kicking his tyre with real violence, it was a real 'John Cleese' moment and I nearly choked on my apple with the hilarity of the scene in front of me. The comic timing continued as I opened the door of my car and made sure he was aware of the fact I had been watching every move.

'Hi, Jamie, nice evening.' I said. There was no reply I crossed the road from the car park towards my house gate. With Jamie now watching me I flicked my apple core towards a bin about ten yards away that was mounted on a lamp post. The apple core spun into a perfect arc and landed with a thump into the centre of the bin, it was a complete fluke - but so what?

'At least I've still got it.' I remarked as I passed through my gate.

Jamie and his family had moved away from Wakefield about four years ago, obviously to Holy Island. Once I had recovered from the coincidence of bumping into Jamie again I explained my problem about the flat battery. Without any hesitation he strode across to his Land Rover fired it up and positioned it near our car. Once again the stranger with the metaphorical tow rope and bacon sandwiches appeared and this time it was a stranger I actually knew. I soon found out that his inability to carry out anything remotely practical on a car hadn't improved. I watched him try and fail several times to open the bonnet of his Landrover before I offered to assist him. Once the bonnet was open we peered inside - there was no sign of a battery.

'I am sure there is one' he expressed. I suddenly felt, in comparison to Jamie as if I was a 'time served' mechanic. The truth is far different. However, I soon found a cover that hid the battery using my newly aquired mechanical confidence. That was about as far as I could go, my jump leads were at home hanging on a nail. It was then that Jamie came up trumps, he did know how to open his boot and emerged with a set of heavy duty jump leads..... we were in action! He hesitated when it came to attaching them to the battteries so I just got on with it. The engine on my car took the charge and despite our slightly uncomfortable history - he had rescued us. As the car sat still, enjoying the surge of power, Jamie's wife, Carol, appeared from around the corner. I had forgotten what a talker she was, half an hour passed as she told Kate every detail of her recent hysterectomy. Jamie shrunk into the background while I untangled the jump leads from our cars. At some point their old neighbours, Pat and Dave came into the conversation and I passed on the news that Dave had died of stomach cancer last year. They didn't seem terribly upset about this information for whatever reason and the conversation came to an end. Our day out at Bamburgh beach was still on the cards and thanks to Jamie, enjoy it we did.

Chapter 53

The next morning my run to the castle was a struggle. My Charles Hawtry legs had returned again but this time without enough energy to push me up the slight slope ahead. I kept going though, breathing heavily, as I lumbered nearer and nearer to my resting bench. As I rounded the final corner I spotted a man propelling himself along in his wheelchair and nearing the stile where I had pushed the sheep back a couple of days ago. We were soon talking; him sitting, me standing and wishing that I could sit in is wheelchair for a much needed rest. Once again I had a companion for the short walk back to the village. Steve was about my age I guessed and was touring the coastline in his motorhome. He had stopped the night as he hadn't felt well enough to leave the island the previous day. The pace at which he moved his chair was very slow and it felt nearly as uncomfortable to walk so slowly beside him as it had been on the run up here. I had to listen carefully due to his impaired speech and heavy accent, both noticeable as he spoke about his motor neurone disease.

He spoke about his journey from his home in Liverpool up through the western side of Scotland, across to Inverness, down through Edinburgh and now moving down the east coast of England. He had left home six weeks previously in April and was expecting to return in October or November. He didn't say so but I knew this was to be the last great adventure for Steve due to his deteriorating condition. Motor Neurone Disease is an unforgiving partner. It felt just right to exchange some words and spend a bit of time with him. We discussed his condition and we talked about his motorhome. It also felt right to say nothing about my lymphoma, my recovery and my remission.

As we approached his mobile home I spotted another wheelchair by the open door which surprised me as I thought he was travelling alone. In fact it was just a comfortable spare wheelchair that he used for sitting around in. We exchanged best wishes and I wished him luck for the remainder of his coastal journey. I wouldn't see him again as he was leaving the island as soon as the tide turned. There is no camping allowed on Holy Island and he was worried about getting into bother. He made a fuss of Minnie, said goodbye and wheeled away. I walked on quite relieved to be walking at my own pace and contemplated the scale of his journey and his determination to complete it. I at least had my Charles Hawtry legs for getting me out on this fine day. They had given me the chance of meeting this brave fellow and as I approached the village I felt quite envious of him. Such a journey must be a great adventure. It is one that I would love to do on my motorbike. The envy soon turned to a realistic sense of gratitude; my condition is in remission and my foreseeable journey is being with Kate and bringing up the children. As I approached the cottage, the gratitude had turned to sorrow for the determined man I had met alone on the coast road with two wheelchairs. Good luck, Steve. May your God go with you.

Chapter 54

Normally on a holiday there are decisions to be made about where to go, when to go and what to do when you arrive. All of those choices become more complex when considered by a family consisting of people with so many different interests. The potential for arguments is, as any parent will know, quite high. Here though, all of those questions are answered by the tide. You only have two choices; stay on the island and take it easy or wait for the causeway to clear before heading to the mainland. Today the road would be safe to cross by 2pm which gave us six hours to get ready. Even then we set off late as we headed towards a town called Alnwick about twenty miles away.

Alnwick is a market town surrounded by lovely countryside, an imposing river and lies about five miles from the coastline. I like market towns, unlike city suburbs, they don't change very much. There is a high street that holds a market two times a week and this street retains its character from one decade to the next. The superstores like 'Currys, Toys 'R' Us, B & Q' and other such eyesores must be about somewhere but there is no room for them in the high street. It is very reassuring to find somewhere without a Tesco or a MacDonalds but such towns do still exist and Alnwick is proof of this. I just hope no Tesco executive ever reads this book or a store would soon appear there. When I finish work and look towards retirement I don't want to live anywhere near a retail park. What we haven't got by then we can live without.

For anybody who believes that the human frame doesn't house a soul just think how you feel when returning home from a retail park. The blame is not entirely down to the style of the place it is mostly to do with the huge number of people seeking bargains.

There is no communication and no interaction. Next time you are in a superstore stand back and hold a door open for a fellow shopper and note the surprise in their voice 'if' they say 'thank you'. Even that simple task would be difficult to carry out due to the presence of those automatic doors. I have noticed many areas of the country where the superstore has wiped out the local trader. That same store then introduces a market type shopping environment. A strange policy that is; destroy the small independent trader, establish a dominance and then try to replicate a shopping environment that people enjoyed in the first place.

The pain these superstores inflict on the community is complete when the chief executive is interviewed on the radio. It is usually a 'he' and he takes the opportunity of mentioning Tesco twenty times in a three minute slot. The interviewer will ask this executive to explain the multi billion profit they have made despite the recession. He isn't honest enough to say that they just put up the prices of the basics and fool the punters by giving them special offers on goods they don't really need. He can't do that and spins a tale about the local community and how it can only benefit from their success. All this explains that depressing feeling experienced as I drive home with my new DVD player. It is the soul that suffers as I recognise my compliance in playing a small part in this subtle act of dominance and profiteering. That is one reason that proves the existence of a soul, mine gets hurt every time I come into contact with the retail park.

When I have to visit them I try everything I can to confound the systems; go in by the wrong entrance, drive around roundabouts the wrong way and take dangerous rides on trolleys. When Michael and Joe were a little younger I found myself in a long queue at MacDonalds attempting to buy two 'Happy Meals'. I noticed that the 'Drive Thru' (as they spell it) was empty. We walked outside and up to the first order window;

'Two Happy Meals and a cup of tea, please.'

The young man was surprised to see me and leant outside the window to take a wider look at the situation. 'Where is your car?' he politely enquired.

'Do you need a car for a drive thru?' I responded.

'I'll ask the manager.' He then disappeared.

A short while later he came back, 'No, apparently you don't.' He said. 'Thanks for your order, move down to the next window and have a nice day.' I manouvered my 'car-less' body and the two children down to the next window, pulled up and waited for the food. By that time a Fiat Punto and a small Suzuki were in the queue behind me.

That's why I like places like Alnwick. I can be trusted to behave there. Towns like that need looking after and long may they prosper. To emphasise the point I spotted a small hardware shop. The owner must have been on a window dressing course lately as the bay fronted Georgian window provided a platform for a very attractively arranged display of hoover bags. It had been carried out with precision. I entered the shop, it smelled of new brushes and dubbin.

'Good afternoon. I need a small nut and bolt about one inch long and five mil' thick to fix one of the bikes'

'Brass or alloy?' came the reply.

'Brass is fine.'

'One or two?'

'Give us two then.'

'That will be twenty four pence, Sir.'

'Thanks very much, perfect. Bye for now.'

'Good day to you.'

I went back there later in the day to buy some batteries for my camera, a small flask and an instant barbeque. That is how it works.

Soon we were sat on the river bank frying up the sausages that we bought from the butcher and taking photographs of Michael and Joe playing with Minnie. Smashing little camera that, it was a bargain in the Curry's sale. I was fortunate, it was the last one and to buy it I had to squeeze myself into the front of the queue narrowly beating a heavily pregnant woman who was luckily distracted by a hungry toddler.

Chapter 55

On the fourth morning my run to the castle was very early, about 6am. There was nobody to talk to or walk back with. The slap of my feet couldn't be heard this time. The awkward running style was still there so I decided to run on the grass which solved the problem. This time it was my ankles that were stiff and inflexible. The forecast wasn't so good for the day ahead so I was pleased to be out while the sun was still in view. With the drop in temperature the sea mist on the horizon had lifted and I could see right across to the Farne Islands. I took a photograph of Minnie who sat on my resting bench. She had taken to the bench as some sort of target we had to achieve each day. She sat next to me even though she would have been more comfortable on the grass. We set off for home with a cooked breakfast looking to be the best plan. We took a different route home via St. Cuthbert's beach and back over the old priory. Magnus Magnusson has written a book about this island. He gives it another name in addition to Holy Island, or Lindisfarne as most people know it. He calls it 'the Cradle Island.' It is easy to see why, it was the birthplace of Celtic Christianity and proved a sanctuary for the bishops for hundreds of years. It was doing just that for me.

Kate meanwhile was still feeling worn out so she rested today and stayed in with Michael, leaving Joe and I to explore a bit further afield. We set off north from the village on our bikes, it was a rough grass track. He was still trying to regain confidence on his bike following a bad bike accident a couple of years ago. I followed on behind him stopping every now and again to pick him up from the grass and encourage him to get back on his bike. The track led to a gate with sand dunes beyond. Our reward for pushing the bikes amongst these huge dunes was a curved bay with golden sand. On view there were large white breakers crashing in and two headlands covered in seabirds. The map showed it to be 'Snipes Bay' and it was deserted apart from the birds, me, Joe and one other family. Joe decided to build an island of rocks so he could walk into the sea without getting his shoes wet. The concentration was impressive as he built his project, not noticing that in doing so his shoes and socks were becoming soaked.

I eventually spoke to the other dad on the beach. He was on holiday with his second wife and three young children. His other daughter, from his first marriage, had stayed at home preparing for a second batch of chemotherapy to help attack ovarian cancer. Maybe a sympathetic ear was all he needed but he talked at length about the pressure of caring for his daughter. He expressed how difficult it was to remain optimistic especially as the first set of treatment hadn't beaten the disease. It was frightening to hear - she had been in exactly the same place as me, in remission. In her case she had the shock of a relapse to cope with and the prospect of having to suffer the treatment all over again. This was of course my greatest fear. He talked on and I watched his lips move without really listening to anything else he had to say. This lasted a couple of minutes before I was able to pay attention once more. I had to distract myself from these thoughts so told him about my condition and that I knew what taking chemotherapy was like. He was somehow reassured by this and talked in a more relaxed way about his daughter until it was time to say goodbye. As Joe and I pushed our bikes back out through the sand dunes I didn't think I had been much help to this man, apart from listening to his story. It did occur to me that cancer was in no way an isolated illness, it can reach anywhere and touch anyone. Even on a sunny isolated beach like this one it cast its shadow over the only two families on it.

Chapter 56

My day wasn't over. Thankfully Kate was feeling a little better and Michael had rekindled his usual spark. I grabbed an hour to myself and took my sketching pencils and a pad down to the tiny fishing harbour. During the time I sat on the steps of the jetty another meeting arose. For goodness sake - wasn't it possible to meet somebody on this island who wasn't ill, meaningful or melancholy. Why couldn't I bump into some bugger who had spent the first four hours of his day on a playstation and the second four hours searching the internet for the best price on a 42 inch plasma screen television? No such luck. Before starting my sketch I walked right to the end of the jetty and was surprised to find a set of steps leading down into the clear water. I sat on the sixth step down, the water lapped up to my feet. I was just about at sea level looking across the bay towards the castle and my resting bench, just visible in the distance. I had just about penciled in this scene and started outlining the three of four lobster boats that were anchored and leaning over to one side, when a shadow cast itself over my drawing pad. A young handsome fellow sat behind me on the fourth step down. He was wearing a black shirt and tie and asked me how I was getting on.

As conversation continued it transpired that 'Jed' as he introduced himself was a fisherman working from this very jetty and had done so since leaving school seven years ago. He worked from the boat 'Jenna' which was at the forefront of my sketch. He hadn't been to work on this particular day. He had been to his Grandma's funeral in Morpeth. She was only seventy one and had experienced a severe stroke to her heart. It appeared to be a loss that was of great measure to him. Jed had decided to spend a few quiet moments this evening at the jetty, the very same place where he spends his working day. Having spent these quiet moments he then chose to sit next to a stranger who was sketching his working boat. We talked on as I sketched a bit further and when the evening became chilly another farewell was exchanged.

As his shadow left my drawing pad I remembered how I had felt when Dad died. The idea of getting into my car, driving down to the motorway, making my way into Leeds and parking up outside my dreary workplace just to think about him was totally implausible, impossible really. Yet this young man headed straight for the place he worked to spend some time remembering his Gran. I imagined that the view, the peace and the sunset provided a fitting eulogy to her. I stayed a while longer and sketched out a few more boats, they were no longer leaning over at such an angle and their masts were gradually pointing higher into the sky as the water came in. The resulting sketch was average enough and would soon provide the basis of something in colour. It sounds ridiculous to think that I could be reminded of somebody I never knew, but when I get around to that painting I will think of Jed and his Grandma.

Chapter 57

I have yet to talk to somebody on this island who has had no effect upon me (with the exception of the newsagent who sold me a tin of chopped tomatoes). I decide that the best option would be to avoid interaction with anybody. That is how I managed to get through the next day - a day without a meaningful meeting with a stranger. Just an ordinary day, a run out with the dog, a trip out to Berwick, (another market town) and later in the day the five of us went out to Snipes Bay. We set up a fire burning some white driftwood and cooked some chicken on the embers. It was quite a challenge trundling through the day without talking to anybody.

Perhaps, shudder the thought, I was an irritation to those I had met. I remember going to visit my youngest brother when he lived in Amsterdam. I was sitting next to a tall Dutchman and in my excitement by mid flight I had found out where he lived, how many kids he had and what he did for a living. In an effort to keep the waning conversation going and ignoring his irritation with me, I said 'I've never met a Dutchman before.'
He nodded forward towards our destination and without looking at me replied, 'You'll meet plenty over there.' Not another word was spoken between us.

Our holiday in this sanctuary was nearly over, only one more day remained before we left the island and headed off home. It had been a great success in comparison to our last holiday. Our final day saw the weather break for the first time and it became colder and wetter. I still felt keen to complete the run to the castle just as I had managed on each of the previous six mornings. This time my ankles and knee joints felt worse as I rose from bed. Usually the aches and pains disappeared as the day progressed, but not today.

I was still limping around well after lunch time. I am not really sure what this chemotherapy has done to me. I don't think it pays to know too much about it. It had given the cancerous cells a right spanking, but whatever oil or lubrication that had been present beforehand was now missing, especially from my waist down. My mum suffers from osteoarthritis and swears by a daily spray of WD40 to her knees. Maybe she isn't as barmy as she sounds. I will try it when I return home though I may get followed about in West Yorkshire by a gay engineer. I looked forward to returning to Holy Island before long, it had been a great week for all of us and it was no more than we deserved.

Chapter 58

More progress came as I was preparing to return to work. I intended to go in for a couple of days per week as a target. Margaret, one of the managers, was working hard trying to cover my tasks as well as her own. Somehow she also found the time to gradually introduce me to activities and events that were going on. She encouraged me to call in at lunchtime or simply to call in for a cup of tea. It meant that on the day when I was due to start work it would be less overpowering for me to cope with.

In the meantime I was just building up my strength and exercising my legs and ankles as much as possible. On my daily walks with Minnie I often passed a council depot which had a huge notice board on its wall. The annoying thing about this blank space was exactly that - it never had anything on it. I decided to go out very early one morning and use this space for a painting.

It was a Saturday and no workmen were about. By six in the morning I was set up with some oil pastels, a step ladder, two apples and a bottle of water. It was a lovely warm morning - Wimbledon was due to start later that day I looked at the blank board for ten minutes as I really didn't have an idea about how to start the project ahead of me. As I stared a bit longer the contours in the hardboard started taking on a shape and there was the outline of a picture. It was to be of a small Cornish village, old tin mines and chimneys in the foreground with sea and cliffs behind. The image on the vacant board started taking a bit of shape. As the local shops opened and people began to leave their houses the local residents approached and passed various comments in favour of my project. They had obviously found the blank notice board as irritating as I did. I stopped for a break about three hours later as my legs wouldn't support me on the stepladder anymore.

About half of the picture had been complete and I had one more day to finish it before the workmen would resume.

The weather was still lovely, the weather programmes had been promising a 'barbeque' summer. At first I thought this may be a government plot to keep the masses happy during this recession but the promise of high temperatures was holding out - so far. A new roof had been built at Wimbledon and everyone at the tennis was desperate for it to rain. It looked like they may be disappointed. I spent another two hours down at the notice board to finish off my Cornish scene and walked back home to make plans for the day.

Our usual Sunday involves a roast dinner for us all and this includes my Mum who joins in. She must have cooked hundreds of Sunday dinners for us lot when she was good on her feet. It was just too hot to stand cooking so instead we took a trip out to a National Trust house along with my two nephews. We played cricket for the sake of doing something different to football, had a tour of the big house and then ate a picnic on the lawn. All far too civilized. Helping the afternoon along were a jazz band playing to the assembled crowd of about one hundred people. They had a really good clarinet player by the sound of it. Some of the people listening were sitting at prim tables enjoying a cream tea while most, like us, sat on a blanket surrounded by bits of apple, half eaten sandwiches and empty milk cartons that had been filled with Ribena. The event was billed as 'Jazz on the Lawn' and we sat and listened to a medley of decent numbers and enjoyed them. They played 'Yellow Bird and another song which included the lyrics

I'm gonna sit right down and right myself a letter
And make believe it came from you
I'll put some kisses on the bottom
And be so glad I got 'em.

I like those words, a great tune and funny with it. The band continued on and now they were so assured of their National Trust audience that they asked if there were any cause for a celebration among the audience. There was little response, none at all from the cream tea section and just one from the milk carton crew. It was a birthday. The band all sidled over to the poor teenager who had been nominated by her mum. 'Happy Birthday' in a rag time style was administered to this poor girl who held her bowed head in both hands riddled with embarrassment. This had a rather dampening effect even on this sunny scene and the band struggled to receive another nomination. I have not been too fond of bands since the 'would be rock star' incident of many years ago and decided to give them a challenge. As they wandered among us, looking for another request, I put my hand up. They were relieved to receive another response and keenly asked what my celebration was, I stood up, took my hat from my head and requested loudly,

'Please sing me something that celebrates my recovery from Chemotherapy and remission from Hodgkin's Lymphoma.'

There followed one of those 'brushwood' moments when all went quiet on the lawn, even the cream teas stopped rattling - just the silent sound of a band in a quandry. By now the audience had swelled to a number of about two hundred and like me they were holding their breath waiting for an answer. The moment must have lasted twenty seconds before the band leader asked rather apologetically if the song 'I will survive' would do.

'No thanks.' I replied. Bad Pete.
'Lets get back to you,' came his response and he turned away from the blanket brigade towards the cream teas hoping for an easier request to celebrate like a messy divorce, a business liquidation or a sex change.

Musicians! Talented, agreed. Spontaneous? I am not so sure. Faced with a real challenge, not much use! Given the predictable they can come up with something that seems original and also rather impressive. Not in this case. Any amount of tunes would have done the job; Somewhere over the rainbow; Who wants to be a millionaire? They could have performed any song, all they needed to do was ask what I would like! Some kind soul eating a cream tea rescued the band by making a request; another birthday. They scurried off to grant her wish, 'Happy Birthday' yet again, this time they adapted it to the style of a Jamaican steel band. Graciously, I waited for them to carve their way through another four tunes before Kate, my two nephews, Michael, Joe and I moved off to set up another game of cricket. As we left, the band leader shouted an apology over for not finding me a tune - that was okay.

Chapter 59

Although the Jazz band didn't come up to scratch I have mentioned many groups and individuals who have. It was only natural to follow their examples and think of ways in which I could help myself. My attempt at painting has been one new adventure. Recording many of the incidents and emotions by writing this book has been another. One of my new targets is to find a publisher and raise some money for the Lymphoma Association and the Wakefield Hospice. I hope all the words I've written will help to achieve this. If you have bought this book and are reading it then the target is being secured. *I thank you very much*. During the tale you may have noticed how important sport has been to me. Not at a professional level, I have never been good enough. Before my illness I had been heard to groan if one of the children wanted to go over to the park and play something - like most Dads in their fifties it can be a much easier prospect to remain in the chair and chat with friends or switch on the television. When I lay in hospital in the 'Gastro ward' as they called it, I resolved never again to groan if one of the kids wanted to go out to play in the park. At that time the chance of ever again being able to enjoy such simple pleasure seemed to be such a remote prospect.

Since becoming ill, one sport in particular I have missed is golf. The best handicap I have ever had is twelve and have been playing off sixteen for the last five years or so. I don't think I will get better than that, I am not sure I ever want to. I played at a municipal club in Wakefield and that weekly round with my mates was a kind of sanctuary away from the busy and chaotic life I led at home and at work. Each week I teamed up with three or four other lads and unlike them could never get upset if a shot went wrong or even if my whole score was ruined by a single hole. I was once having a great round - almost playing to par when I took thirteen shots getting out of a bunker on the eighth hole. By the fourth shot I was seeing the funny side of it - especially the fact that I was still counting. I have listened to my mates curse and swear, watched them break their clubs and on one occasion Jamie threw his whole bag and trolley into a bush. I tend not to concentrate too hard on golf and that is probably why I don't improve much. I am happy with my lot as I stroll around the course. I usually score in the high eighties, some good shots, some bad, most of them are okay and just one shot that is brilliant. My casual attitude is further strengthened by watching the others get in such an aggressive state over a missed putt, a difficult lie or a lost ball.

As a consequence golf has been sometimes very amusing. There is a competition each Sunday morning which is treated seriously and on two of these occasions I was doing very well. Even I was taking it seriously, which was a mistake. On the sixth green I was eyeing up a longish putt and feeling convinced this was to be a birdie. I couldn't quite see the lie of the green and normally this wouldn't bother me, I would just walk up give the ball a poke and hope it would go in. I decided to take a bit more care than normal and retreated backwards to see if the direction I needed to use would be come clearer. As I concentrated on the 'lie' of this putt, the ground suddenly disappeared from under my feet as I fell into a deep bunker. It served me right for thinking too much.

Another time was in the Monthly Medal. I had been playing well and somehow the round had yet to be spoiled by a huge score on any single hole. My friend Nigel pointed out that if I was to par the last hole I would score a seventy nine. That would be the best round I had ever managed. I did achieve the par, signed my card and put it in the competition box. Nigel was very keen that I should win a competition at last and visited the golf club midweek to check the results. My name wasn't even in the top ten, let alone at the winners end. He made some enquiries about my wonderful score and rang me that evening;

'Hi, Pete. I went down today for the Monthly Medal results.'

'Really?' I replied, feigning interest. I was actually quite excited. I had never won the monthly medal in four years of trying and as it was Christmas week the prize was a hamper of wines and spirits.

'You were disqualified, you burk. I can't believe what you did!

He went on to explain that I had written my name down on the card as 'Monthly Medal' and even though it was the best round of the day the club secretary didn't know who it belonged to, so it was not counted. I was called 'M & M' for a few months after that by anybody in the club who heard the tale, which was just about everybody.

On another Sunday morning I turned up slightly the worse for wear after a late night with friends. The 'tee off' time had to be split into two as there were six of us playing. It was busy at the club and people were queuing waiting to play down the first fairway. Our turn came and I set off with the first group towards the distant flag. After walking two hundred yards I had failed to find my ball and asked Sean if he had seen it.

'What are you talking about, you haven't hit your shot yet, you're playing in the match behind!'

I had to walk all the way back to the first tee to be met by hoots of laughter and derisive comments from all of the waiting golfers who had witnessed my forgetful moment.

Two weeks later my mates started laughing and pointing as my car rolled into the car park. Thinking my exhaust pipe must be hanging off I jumped out of the car only to find my golf shoes still on the roof. I had been late again and in the rush I put the shoes on the car roof, forgot about them, jumped in the car and drove off. The rubber studs had helped them cling to the top of the car for the two mile journey to the golf club. It never happens to Tiger Woods, does it? I have really missed the golf, it is too much to expect just yet. Walking six miles is beyond me.

I have been very disappointed in my golfing mates with the exception of one, Nigel. He has had a lot of problems of his own this year but somehow managed to keep in touch by text or phone and by making the occasional visit. Two weeks ago he invited me out to play. He must have been working that day for the arranged time was five in the morning. I turned up pretty much the same as always just a touch late and fairly confused wondering what the next few hours would bring. He was stood waiting next to the only other car in the car park. Unbelievably I had actually forgotten my golf clubs so we would have to share his. There was something else unbelievable. I have made many references to friends who have helped us along the way by comparing something they have done to giving me a bacon sandwich. Nigel soon forgave me for the fact that I would have to share his clubs and produced a batch of hot bacon sandwiches in tin foil.

I enjoyed that morning, there was no way I was going to get all the way round and there was no way I could play to a sixteen handicap. In fact we managed to walk, talk and play twelve holes before my legs became an unco-ordinated jangle. I enjoyed every moment on that quiet misty morning, I picked eight ounces of mushrooms and even the squirrels appeared to stop their summer jobs for a minute or two as they waited for me to pass along the fairway.

As for the golf - well my limbs felt awkward and out of kilter with my arms, I hit lots of terrible shots, mostly bad ones, two or three good ones and one that was brilliant. That will do for me. As we said goodbye the car park was just starting to fill up with a few other early morning players. We exhanged the promise of another match sometime soon and then Nigel presented me with the Ben Sayers driver that I had been using. I was delighted with that gift and the one brilliant shot that I had made with it from the tenth tee. Most of all I appreciated the bacon sandwiches. Nigel wouldn't have understood why this simple breakfast meant so much.

Chapter 60

The day arrived for my return to work. Despite the gentle week I had in store and the consideration shown to me by the teams I work with, I felt frightened. I didn't really know what to do when I arrived. I sat in the car park turned off the ignition and opened the door. My next action was to return to my car seat and shut the door. I took several deep breaths and tried again - this time it worked. My first call was the head office where my boss, Andrea had kindly arranged a desk in her room to help me get going. I received a warm welcome and a hot drink before I tackled my first trip down the corridor towards the people I hadn't seen in nearly a year. They were all working at their desks as I made my appearance. I was very surprised how pleased they were to see me but also glad to return to the quiet of Andrea's office and stare at my blank computer screen. I couldn't even remember how to turn it on. I decided to stare at my blank diary instead. Eventually, with help, I found my way into the email account. Margaret had been filtering them, replying to people and dealing with most of the issues so as not to over burden me on my first day. She's lovely she is. All I had to deal with were a few interesting things that could help reawaken my sleepy brain. There were lots of 'welcome back' notes sent from all sorts of colleagues in the region and across the country.

My second visit of the day was to our base in West Leeds. I walked into the staff room, there were only two people there as the rest of the team were either in class or out with students. In total there are fifty people working for Vine, which is the name of the service we run. Inevitably with a team that size there are going to be a few people with whom it is difficult to get on with. One of the people sitting in the staff room came into this category. As I walked in he raised his eyes, saw me and returned to whatever he was reading. I felt very angry that after such a long absence that he could be this dismissive. I have experienced rudeness like this many times before my illness and possibly on occasions I had deserved such treatment. Not now though - not on my first day back at work. The effect of his act wormed its way right under my skin and I knew if I didn't deal with it straight away it would carry on eating away at my confidence. I waited until break time and visited his class room. I invited him outside and he seemed very bemused by my request. I asked him to imagine how he would feel after nearly a year away from work battling with cancer and consider how he may feel on his first day at back at work. He offered some sort of response which did little to redeem his previous actions. In reply to that I said

'I think you need to know that your reaction was the last thing I needed today. You also need to know that after all I have been through to get back here, within a few seconds you made me feel like a pile of crap.'

He tried to say that he actually did bother greeting me, that I had just misunderstood. Maybe so. I am able to apologise if I get something wrong. It doesn't make any difference anyway. The fact was that this illness had made me react differently to those around me who seemed keen to dish out a hard time. There was no space for this anymore and I felt pleased about my instinctive reaction. This was an isolated case and not repeated with any of the other forty nine people I was to meet during the course of the week. My final visit of the day was over to Margaret's centre a few miles away. It was such an odd sensation. It felt like a new job, a new job in which everyone already knew my name and the pictures of my kids were already on the wall. I still felt pretty clueless as to what I needed to do. My blank diary gave me no clue about the tasks ahead. Just as I was wondering which way to turn, my bookcase collapsed. This was a greeting I could cope with. This timely shock was to produce a nice easy little task, picking up files, papers and text books and putting them back in an order that would help me remember all of projects and challenges that this job had thrown at me in the recent past.

Chapter 61

The excitement continued, the very next day a hand written note popped through the letter box, it was from a company called Keepmoat who were subcontractors to the local council. It read:

If you are the gentleman who painted the picture on our notice board, please contact us. Thank you.

I didn't bother ringing the number on the note straight away. It seemed a rather formal note and I was slightly worried that I may land myself in bother for trespass or damage due to graffiti. Much earlier on I mentioned the incident when I had made a mistake locking up my motorbike in Leeds. In fact I hadn't locked mine up at all, for some reason I had locked somebody else's bike. On that occasion I was met by a man who had been waiting for me to turn up. He was very angry and understandably so. I managed to wriggle out of that one by explaining that I had a bike share arrangement with my friend, Alan. That was true. I explained that he was quite a bit older than me. That was true also. I then went on to say that he was inclined to daft things and it was he who had locked up the wrong bike, not me. This wasn't true, but it seemed to calm this animated and energetic biker who had drunk six cups of coffee waiting for me to arrive and was now four hours late for his next appointment. It is a side of me I am not proud of but it saved me a punch and let's face it - he had no chance of ever meeting Alan. As I pondered this letter from 'Keepmoat' a similar plan came to mind. I could ring the lady who had written to me and if trouble was looming I would instantly blame my eldest son, Sam. He is studying sculpture at Bath University, which is miles away. It would be natural enough to say that he did it when he came home for the weekend and that I would pass on the note to him. Blooming art students! No end of trouble.

I rang and immediately felt guilty that I had hatched such a deceitful story. The lady I spoke to was called Claire and seemed delighted to track me down. They were in fact so pleased with the picture that they had removed it from the depot and put it in their head office in Castleford. She had tracked me down by asking those living close to the compound if they had seen who had carried out the deed. They had, but these neigbours didn't know my name. They had just seen me painting. They had also seen me leaving and entering my house when I was out with Minnie, so knew where I lived. Claire went on to explain that the Wakefield Express were doing an article called 'The Mystery Artist of Horbury.' This was to be a bit of fun and I looked forward to becoming an amateur 'Banksie' for the day. Claire even asked me if I would be prepared to paint some more pictures around the depot.

When I told Kate about the note and the phone call she decided it was too good an opportunity to miss. Here was a chance to gain some much needed publicity for the Hospice and the Lymphoma Association. Kate rang the paper and spragged on me as being the mystery artist. Within a day or two I was photographed along with two workers from the Keepmoat Company standing next to the painting itself. The publicity worked quite well as the story in the paper provided quite a lot of information abut the hospice, the art group and their day services. Most importantly it went on to explain that you don't have to be terminally ill to go there and benefit from their activities. Over the next few weeks I enjoyed the life of a local celebrity and was recognised by a school caretaker, a lady called Joan who runs the bingo at the working men's club and Karen who is the cashier at the bank. That was the most interest I've ever received from the 'surf boarding Howard' or any of his colleagues at the Halifax. As I visited my local shops in the third week wondering if a fourth person would recognise my face, I received a copy of an email that my mate Alan had sent to the journalist who wrote the newspaper story. Here it is in full.

I am outraged by your story 'Mystery Artist Revealed' in a recent issue of the Wakefield Express and wish to protest in the strongest possible terms. As you will recall, your piece centred on (and featured a photograph of) a Mr. Peter Vickers and his claim to have painted the eight foot wide picture on the council depot in Horbury. Mr. Vickers is not responsible, I am and his claim is completely bogus.

For some time now, Mr. Vickers has been emulating me, posing as me and claiming credit for the things I have done.. Like him, I have been ill. In my case I've had (and have still got) Manually Induced Blindness Syndrome (MIBS) which is the reason why, in the art world, I am known as 'Wanksie.' The condition means of course that I have to paint with the brush between my toes. I also do Christmas cards, by the way.

Despite strenuous efforts to get the same condition as me, Mr. Vickers failed to produce MIBS in himself, but somehow contrived to get Hodgkin's Lymphoma. I created the art work in the dead of night, aided by my wife who guided my foot as well as deterring me from engaging in Manually Induced Blindness Activities for an hour or so.

Let's have accuracy back in local newspaper journalism!

I look forward to your response and to a larger feature about my good self in a forthcoming issue of the paper. As a way of compensating me and setting the record straight, just to rub Mr. Vickers' nose in it, I would be quite keen to have him in the picture as well.

Yours sincerely, Alan 'Wanksie' Whinthrop.

I enjoyed this and wondered if the journalist would print it in the following week's paper. It served me right anyway and he had certainly got his own back for the time I blamed him about the motorbike incident. I bought the paper again the folowing Friday and there was no mention of Alan and his MIBS condition. I guess it was just a little too near the knuckle for the local rag. A shame.

Chapter 62

This can be a short chapter, I expect it will be. It could be much longer. If it becomes lengthy then I have been unable to focus upon the most important parts of this journey. I will trust these pages to do their best by recalling the times that have seemed to be the very worst and the very best. However long I live and hopefully this will be a long time, I will never be able to forget my alien and the awful Captain Chemo. I have been amazed at the kindness and support given by people who had no real need to care. I will also remember the lack of interest shown by some people whom I thought we could rely upon. I have been so surprised that this illness has given me such a beating yet at the same time generated so many important memories, so many emotions and so many reasons for me to keep going.

I have learned to appreciate and benefit from the specialist help I have received especially from the nursing team, the medical team and those providing a more alternative and gentle approach. The encouragement received from my colleagues at work has been a crucial part in my recovery. I am lucky enough to have many friends that have provided consistent support, ideas and visits. I have sat back, listened and been inspired by the thoughts and actions of the children. I have been cared for by my close family and enjoyed regular visits from them as they travelled from towns all over this country and from Spain, France and Ireland. My feelings have been tested to the limit and all those hidden emotions emerging from 1993 have appeared on a high ridge waving a big red flag at me. It has been good to deal with that, at last! There have been many references to sport, recollections of single events, to our dog and to incidental meetings or encounters. All of these have maintained a strategic and important piece of territory within my tiny empire as the boundaries were invaded and occupied.

The benefit of writing about these moments has proved to be a greater therapy than anything else that I could have possibly purchased or subscribed to. Applying my pen to paper with just my thoughts in between has been an immense help, much greater than any support gained from a white British Home Stores tea set, a lighted candle or a bottle of whisky.

The very worst events include the numerous times when Kate had to cling on to me throughout the night, when my temperature was so high, my sickness so persistent and no bed was available in the hospital - all we were offered was a chair in Accident and Emergency. These were the times when we held on to each other, never really knowing what the next hour would bring.

Those hours taught me how to appreciate two special facts. Kate is the last I see at night and the first I see in the morning. No matter what problems we face during the day those two assurances are all I am ever likely to need. I wrap my arms around her tightly, holding on to the frail and tiny frame of my lovely girl, the woman who laid all before her, conquered her fears and trusted that I would get better. Kate has been the most important member of those populating the events and reflections making up this story, she has been the most helpful, she has been the hardest worker and the most appreciated. She is the most special person I will ever meet.

Chapter 63

The final chapter is written at the beginning of August. Spooky - but it is exactly a year ago since Kate and I were struggling to get home from our holiday to begin our visits to various doctors. Today started with a trip to the local hairdresser so the boys and I can get trimmed up before we venture upon the long road to Cornwall again. There is a new shop at the end of the road, it used to be a poodle parlour, we thought it might be worth giving it a try. I was the last to sit in the chair having listened to the hairdresser chatting away to Michael and Joe. Huge amounts of hair dropped onto the floor below them. When my turn came I slid into the chair and as expected she chatted away;

'What thick hair your boys have, I can see now where they get it from.'
'I'm pleased to hear you say that. Just a couple of months ago I didn't have any at all' I cheerfully responded.

As hairdressers do she soon ascertained the reason for my baldness and as she spoke further I noticed her rather sweet and uninformed knowledge about the illness. As my haircut neared its completion, she came out with this observation:

'You'd be amazed how many people sit in that chair with exactly the same thing as you have had. Cancer! It's ever so popular these days.'

I am now musing over this comment as I tackle my second job of the day. I am sitting in a corridor at Pontefract Hospital. The allotted appointment time with my consultant has long passed as I await the results of my blood test. Whatever the outcome I feel well enough to drive back home and complete my third job.

We are ready to load the car, wave at Pat and set off to finish that holiday. It's as if we are on rewind and I am scanning the rapidly moving events of this last year. I am sorely tempted to delay this entry for one more hour and include the results of my blood test, the physical examination on my lymph nodes and the outcome of the discussion with my consultant. I won't bother. This is how it will be every three months and the forseeable future. I'd better get used to it! As long as these meetings continue to take place in small clinical rooms off this corridor - I'll not be too worried. If he ever invites me back into the room with the brown leather settee and orders me a decent cuppa, then I will probably faint.

If the Hodgkin's Lymphoma returns it will create two situations. Firstly it will frighten me stiff, there is not much more to say about that. Secondly it will demand that I once again have to draw upon all the resources, skills and support that have been discovered over the last twelve months. It will be 'Hodgkin's Choice' for me. I must admit that the sum of all these parts have resulted in a rich experience. I am certain that I am not the first cancer patient to have said that - at least not among those of us who have survived! Here is the question; *given the choice, would I go through it all again?* If my current state of remission should ever relapse then one character among the many would emerge with a menacing presence. It's my alien.

Even as I calmly sit here in this row of plastic hospital chairs the idea of his return has sent my whole body into a shiver. The elderly man sitting next to me in this crowded hospital corridor must fear I have swine flu. What was that question again? Oh yes. The answer is not an easy one

'Given the choice, I don't think I could! I'll have to wait and see.'

With more than a little thanks to the population

Ian for the constant encouragement.
Bev for the fortnightly letter.
Paul for the visits, the jokes and decorating the living room.
Gareth Southgate.
Father Mark and Father Bernard.
The staff at Michael and Joe's school for their care
Dennis and Kay, who know what it is all about.
Norman and Louise for the walks the talks and the understanding.
Catherine and Anthony for the constant support, help and games
of snooker
Gillian Shelton and Ben
Margaret at Vine in Leeds (who could do with a page to herself.)
Dave for the proof reading.
My boss Andrea for kind support.
Jennie for all the presents and visits.
Aileen and Lily.
Kathy.
Andy Palin for the extraordinary welcome back to work.
Russell (my buddy) and Sarah
Marilyn, for the inspiring card
Dominic the shed mover.
Malcolm and Joanne.
Pat our good neighbour and her husband, Dave - who didn't make
it this far.
Steve Ward for never forgetting to keep in touch.
Michelle and Chad for their visits and chicken soup
Bill and Stella for all the support and all the miles.
Vin and Karen
Janet, for her enthusiasm after reading the first few chapters
Chris for regular contact and all the prayers.
Jill and Craig for the Mazda, the lifts, the red hat, the wig and the
'number 1' haircut.

Ann and Andy for seeing me through that night in hospital and much more.

Catherine for never failing to ask

Steve the Fireman, for doing the same

Carl at the allotment.

Thornes Juniors for keeping me going during the winter.

Mark, Juliette, 'Kebab' George and Katherine

Nigel and his bacon sandwich

David and Lynn Isles

Hugh, for helping mend the tap, twice.

The rest of the Vine team in Leeds.

The Vine students for cards and gifts

To Rick for the long journey from Lands End and the reliable nightly phone calls when I was in 'Gastro ward'

Motor Home Steve - who should be home by now.

Julie in the butchers.

Joan the newsagent.

Earnshaws Greengrocers.

Mike at the Deli'

Michael at the DIY shop.

Dr. Maynard, Dr. Hunter and Pauline at Orchard Croft surgery.

Claire and Simone for a free haircut and free advice.

Alan and Kate who were constantly helping.

Catherine the homeopath for her understanding and those little white tablets.

The dog walkers.

Pat and Phil for good cheer and the visits.

Jim and Paula for kindness to us all.

Dave and Marion who understood perfectly.

Judy and Margaret for keeping in touch.

Sharon, Claire, Rachel, Nannette, Catherine and Laura and all of the staff on Dr. Jackson ward at Pontefract Hospital

Dr. Wright, Dr. Umran and Sue, the secretary. (See you in three months!)
Carol, Ann , Dilys, Carol, Anne, Dilys, Karen and all the staff at the Wakefield Hospice
The Hospice users, volunteers and Chaplains
The friendly staff at the Lymphoma Association
Nigel for the bacon sandwiches.
Mum for the things only mums can do.
My Dad, who would have enjoyed the read.
Barry for all the pedalling – Lands End to John 'O' Groats.
www.regina.bolena.com
Pauline for dedicated support
Andy for helping design the cover
Bob and Pat at Nice Pond
Pen2print, especially Tom and Charlotte
Dave for travelling from Spain and buying me the hat.
Louise for the lifts and givng the kids some tea.
Sam, Rosie Michael and Joe for surviving a horrible year
Kate, of course.
Dave and Marion for advice, support and sunflowers.
Lynne Edwards for buying the first book!
All those who pushed through the turnstile into my tiny empire
Captain Chemo for only appearing once

And finally, my alien who appeared too often.